11+ Verbal Reasoning Success

Age 6–7

Age 7–8

Age 8–9

Age 9–10

Age 10–11

Assessment Papers

Alison Primrose and Alison Head

Sample page

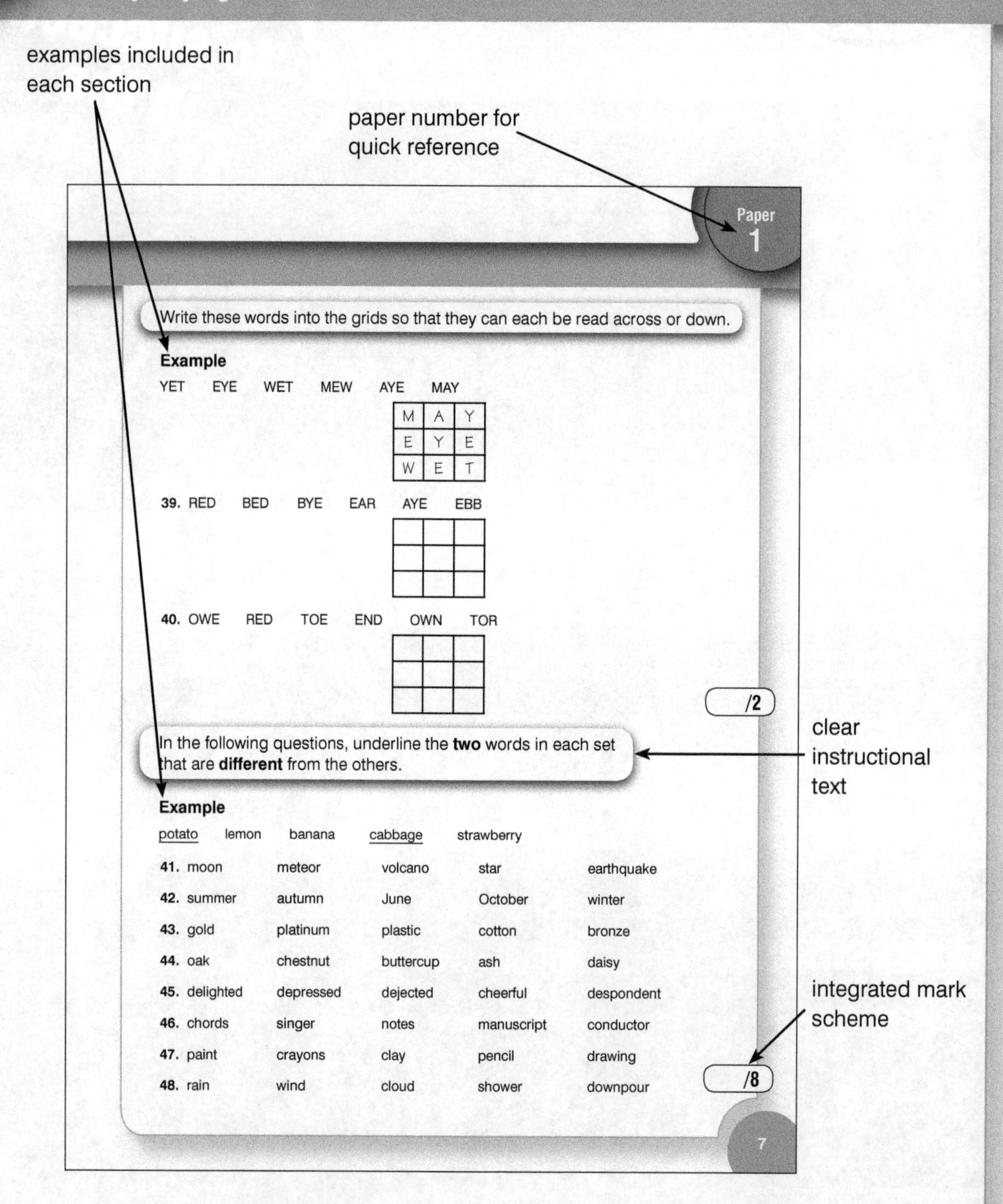

examples included in each section
paper number for quick reference
Paper 1
Write these words into the grids so that they can each be read across or down.
Example
YET EYE WET MEW AYE MAY
M A Y
E Y E
W E T
39. RED BED BYE EAR AYE EBB
40. OWE RED TOE END OWN TOR
/2
In the following questions, underline the two words in each set that are different from the others.
Example
potato lemon banana cabbage strawberry
41. moon meteor volcano star earthquake
42. summer autumn June October winter
43. gold platinum plastic cotton bronze
44. oak chestnut buttercup ash daisy
45. delighted depressed dejected cheerful despondent
46. chords singer notes manuscript conductor
47. paint crayons clay pencil drawing
48. rain wind cloud shower downpour
/8
7
clear instructional text
integrated mark scheme

PAPER 1

In the following questions, underline the **two** words, **one** from each set, that have a **similar meaning**.

Example

(car, take, jump) (chair, leap, drive)

1. (route, hunt, travel) (location, treasure, search)
2. (wait, pressure, help) (encourage, assist, action)
3. (teach, read, lessons) (learn, instruct, copy)
4. (dream, slumber, rest) (solitary, bed, sleep)
5. (jump, run, crawl) (skip, ski, sprint)
6. (heavy, burden, worry) (parcel, load, package)
7. (wallet, cash, purse) (money, cheque, receipt)
8. (mischief, trouble, worry) (misery, anxiety, dilemma)

/8

Underline **one** word from the list in brackets that goes equally well with both pairs of words outside the brackets.

Example

(ribbon, present, play, theatre, party)

gift, token show, demonstrate

9. (arrange, book, state, page)
   novel, volume reserve, order
10. (tack, leaf, stick, root)
    glue, attach twig, branch
11. (rest, perch, bench, stream)
    balance, sit bream, trout
12. (direct, guide, preserve, long)
    instruct, tell candid, frank
13. (low, smart, lace, bow)
    ribbon, trim bend, stoop

14. (cut, wound, strain, looped)
coiled, spiralled   injury, lesion

15. (criticise, object, refuse, fight)
rubbish, scraps   deny, decline

16. (lightning, zip, lock, stem)
bolt, fasten   tress, strand

/8

In the following questions, move **one** letter from the first word and add it to the second word to make two new words. Do **not** move any other letters. Write **both** new words, which **must make sense**, on the lines provided.

Example

ta**b**le   reed → tale breed

17. treason   raining → ____________ ____________

18. crotchet   though → ____________ ____________

19. waist   desert → ____________ ____________

20. frond   book → ____________ ____________

21. broom   rink → ____________ ____________

22. flown   keel → ____________ ____________

/6

In the first set of three words, the middle word has been made from letters in the other two words. Complete the second set of words in the **same** way to make the missing words, **which must make sense**. Write your answers on the lines provided.

Example

fast (tea) real   leaf (fir) hire

23. care (ice) shin   rope (__________) room

24. stop (pear) real   loaf (__________) load

25. shall (leap) yelp charm (________) host

26. poles (loopy) poppy racer (________) trace

27. could (load) aloud louse (________) under

28. thief (fire) rise moist (________) lent

29. shore (ruse) rushed tulle (________) punter

30. grain (grape) preen smile (________) natty

/8

In these questions, the pairs of letters are **linked** in some way. On the answer lines provided, write the **two** letters that complete the second pair, following the same pattern as the first. The alphabet has been provided to help you.

A B C D E F G H I J K L M N O P Q R S T U V W X Y Z

Example

BY is to **EV** as **HS** is to KP

31. **BC** is to **EF** as **VW** is to ________

32. **CF** is to **IL** as **OR** is to ________

33. **TQ** is to **PM** as **BY** is to ________

34. **DC** is to **DA** as **PO** is to ________

35. **AY** is to **WU** as **SQ** is to ________

36. **ZW** is to **YS** as **RO** is to ________

37. **DB** is to **EA** as **QO** is to ________

38. **BZ** is to **DZ** as **FD** is to ________

/8

Write these words into the grids so that they can each be read across or down.

Example

YET EYE WET MEW AYE MAY

M	A	Y
E	Y	E
W	E	T

39. RED BED BYE EAR AYE EBB

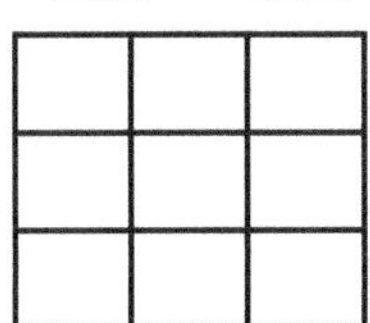

40. OWE RED TOE END OWN TOR

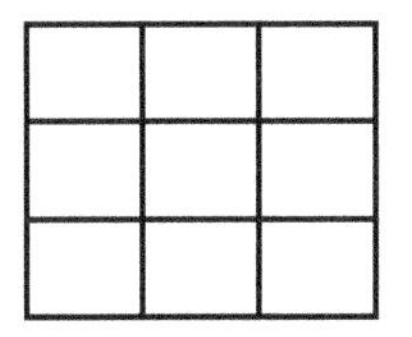

/2

In the following questions, underline the **two** words in each set that are **different** from the others.

Example

potato lemon banana cabbage strawberry

41.	moon	meteor	volcano	star	earthquake
42.	summer	autumn	June	October	winter
43.	gold	platinum	plastic	cotton	bronze
44.	oak	chestnut	buttercup	ash	daisy
45.	delighted	depressed	dejected	cheerful	despondent
46.	chords	singer	notes	manuscript	conductor
47.	paint	crayons	clay	pencil	drawing
48.	rain	wind	cloud	shower	downpour

/8

In each of the following questions, letters stand for numbers. Work out the answer to each sum. Write your answer as a **letter** on the line provided.

Example

If A = 2, B = 3, C = 4, D = 5, E = 6 and F = 8

what is the answer to this sum written as a letter? D + B = F

If A = 2, B = 5, C = 9, D = 14 and E = 21, what is the value of:

49. $D \times A - E + A =$ ________

50. $E + B + A - D =$ ________

51. $B \times B - D - C =$ ________

If A = 15, B = 8, C = 10, D = 30 and E = 3, what is the value of:

52. $D - A + E - B =$ ________

53. $D \div E + B - C =$ ________

54. $C \times E - A =$ ________

/6

Change the first word of the third pair in the same way as the other pairs, to give a new word. Write the answers on the lines provided.

Example

tray, dray   tram, dram   trip, drip

55. time, emit   live, evil   stop, ________

56. seat, eats   pram, ramp   each, ________

57. dame, made   face, cafe   cape, ________

58. lose, loose   weds, weeds   nose, ________

59. pinch, chip   patch, chap   ninth, ________

60. veil, live   meal, lame   read, ________

/6

/60

PAPER 2

In the following questions, underline the **two** words, **one** from each set, that are **opposite in meaning**.

Example

(talk, run, whisper) (sprint, shout, speak)

1. (grow, rise, up) (fall, build, lose)
2. (mend, cut, sharp) (blade, blunt, edge)
3. (create, model, marvel) (design, destroy, plan)
4. (argue, order, accept) (resent, reject, resist)
5. (confer, congratulate, contact) (commiserate, consider, convince)
6. (capture, pursue, reach) (cultivate, purchase, release)
7. (considerable, considerate, concerned) (negligible, nonexistent, gone)
8. (assert, asset, assist) (restrain, hold, hinder)

/8

In these questions, the word in capitals has had a group of **three** letters taken out. These three letters spell another word, without changing the order. Write the **three-letter** words on the lines provided. The sentences need to make sense.

Example

CABE and beans were her favourite vegetables. BAG

9. They wished them every HAPESS. ____________
10. The WR was very cold! ____________
11. Tom was PLING the bulbs. ____________
12. Their new AVAN was quite luxurious for holidays. ____________
13. She enjoyed reading all about the latest FIONS. ____________
14. The children all had a part in the Christmas POMIME. ____________
15. They cleared the rubbish that was FING the pond. ____________
16. They made crumble with the RARB. ____________

/8

In the following sentences, a word of **four letters** is hidden across the **end** of one word and the **start** of the next word. Write the hidden words on the lines provided. The letter order must **not** be changed.

Example

The shop was la**st op**en on Tuesday. stop

17. He really enjoyed his visit that day. ______
18. Come and see us all again. ______
19. They went to the town early. ______
20. Find a place for me to stay! ______
21. They always have strawberries with cream. ______
22. The fish are not rising to the bait. ______
23. Can we alter the date? ______
24. When is he going to address the crowd? ______

/8

Find the missing **pair of letters** in each sequence. The alphabet has been provided to help you.

A B C D E F G H I J K L M N O P Q R S T U V W X Y Z

Example

MO MK OQ KI QS

25. AB AD AG ______ AP
26. DC HG LK PO ______
27. ZX AC VT EG ______ IK

28. ZU YT XS ______ VQ

29. AB DF HK ______ SX

30. ML MO MJ MQ ______ MS

/6

Rearrange all the capital letters to form a correctly spelt word that will complete these sentences sensibly. Write the words on the answer lines.

Example

His pet rabbit was hungry so he fed him a juicy TOCARR. CARROT

31. The orchestra played the famous PNYSYOMH. ______

32. Sam went to RTOSPUP his home team. ______

33. The train arrived CULYPANTUL. ______

34. The CLEMAS carried heavy loads across the desert. ______

35. It was GRUPONI with rain. ______

36. The WERSPEPAN was delivered every day. ______

37. The NOLIDSARFEG were darting around over the pond. ______

38. The weather SCROFTEA predicted stormy weather. ______

/8

Find the **relationship** between the **numbers** in the first two sets of brackets. The numbers in the third set of brackets are **related in the same way**. Find the missing number and add it to the final set of brackets.

Example

(6 [48] 8) (9 [45] 5) (7 [21] 3)

39. (17 [6] 11) (21 [2] 19) (18 [______] 7)

40. (3 [27] 9) (4 [32] 8) (7 [______] 6)

41. (15 [5] 3) (77 [7] 11) (81 [________] 9)

42. (2 [6] 2) (4 [18] 2) (7 [________] 2)

43. (16 [1] 3) (25 [2] 3) (64 [________] 3)

/5

To complete these questions, you need to **balance** the **numbers** on each side of the equation. Start by working out the calculation on the left. Next, find the missing number that will give the **same total** on the right-hand side.

Example

$10 \times 6 \div 5 = 22 + 3 - [13]$

44. $(24 + 3) - 9 = (8 + 14) -$ ________

45. $6 \times 8 \div 12 = (12 +$ ________ $) - 16$

46. $11 \times 4 \div 2 = ($ ________ $+ 15) - 8$

47. $\frac{(16 + 4)}{2} =$ ________ $\times (2 + 3)$

48. $3 \times (2 \times 4) =$ ________ $\times (3 \times 2)$

/5

Change the first word of the third pair in the same way as the other pairs, to give a new word. Write the answers on the lines provided.

Example

tray, dray tram, dram trip, *drip*

49. plan, plain man, main pant, ________

50. stream, streamer firm, firmer burn, ________

51. till, stills lip, slips lot, ________

52. camper, cap barter, bat canter, ________

53. winter, wine filter, file wander, ______________

54. tip, tipple lit, little pad, ______________

/6

In the following questions, underline the **two** words, **one** from each set, that will complete each sentence in the most sensible way.

Example

Head is to (face, arm, neck) as foot is to (leg, knee, thigh).

55. Hot is to (kettle, cold, tea) as fast is to (win, hunger, slow).

56. Crimson is to (paint, colour, red) as azure is to (haze, blue, sky).

57. Day is to (sun, light, awake) as night is to (bed, dark, owls).

58. Minute is to (time, hand, hour) as centimetre is to (mile, distance, ruler).

59. Bird is to (feather, egg, wings) as fish is to (chips, sea, scale).

60. Summer is to (holiday, season, winter) as Monday is to (work, holiday, day).

/6

/60

PAPER 3

In the first set of three words, the middle word has been made from letters in the other two words. Complete the second set of words in the **same** way to make the missing words, **which must make sense**. Write your answers on the lines provided.

Example

fast (tea) real   leaf (fir) hire

1. slot (most) loam   lane (________) soap
2. cream (ladle) dealt   carat (________) green
3. round (trot) often   ousts (________) tents
4. find (dine) fend   heir (________) drew
5. stalk (leak) wreak   crawl (________) spoon
6. shed (peas) part   leek (________) damp
7. towed (wrote) wrist   salty (________) reach
8. dream (read) march   flair (________) tower

/8

These four words have been written as **number codes**, but one of the codes is missing. The words and codes are not necessarily in the same order. Write the answers to the questions on the lines provided.

READ	DEER	DRAW	WEED
4331	1354	4152	

9. Pick out the code for READ. ________
10. Pick out the word with the number code 4331. ________
11. Which word is missing a code? ________
12. What is the code for the word in answer 11? ________

SHEET HEATS STEAM SHAME

34156 32561 21543

13. Pick out the code for SHAME. ______________

14. Pick out the word with the number code 21543. ______________

15. Which word is missing a code? ______________

16. What would be the code for TEAMS? ______________

/8

Underline the **two** words, **one** from each set, that when put together make one new, correctly spelt word. **The word from the group on the left always comes first.**

Example

(run, <u>use</u>, give) (take, <u>less</u>, red)

17. (ask, for, skip) (hood, get, mine)

18. (car, wrap, bar) (foot, age, gain)

19. (off, under, in) (hill, ice, space)

20. (dream, fort, dark) (night, light, spray)

21. (for, win, won) (take, make, age)

22. (grain, bran, dust) (dish, plate, porch)

23. (host, guard, guest) (door, man, age)

24. (board, cut, from) (lass, free, ice)

/8

In these questions, the pairs of letters are **linked** in some way. On the answer lines provided, write the **two** letters that complete the second pair, following the same pattern as the first. The alphabet has been provided to help you.

A B C D E F G H I J K L M N O P Q R S T U V W X Y Z

Example

BY is to **EV** as **HS** is to KP

25. **DW** is to **FU** as **HS** is to ______________

26. **EC** is to **GA** as **OM** is to ______________

27. **BY** is to **BE** as **KH** is to ______________

28. **HJ** is to **GC** as **OQ** is to ______________

29. **BZ** is to **DB** as **WU** is to ______________

30. **XU** is to **TR** as **OL** is to ______________

31. **LJ** is to **KI** as **BZ** is to ______________

32. **AX** is to **BT** as **CP** is to ______________

/8

33. Polly, Anna, Faizah and Soo often visit a local café.

If the weather is cold, Faizah orders hot chocolate. Polly always orders a strawberry milkshake. Anna and Soo sometimes have a plate of chips. Each child only orders one item from the menu at each visit to the café.

If these statements are true, only one of the following statements **must** be true. Which one?

A Faizah never orders chips.

B Anna and Soo always place the same order.

C Polly is the only friend who places the same order every time they visit.

D Polly and Faizah never order the same thing.

E Polly does not like hot chocolate. ______________

/1

34. Read the statements below, then answer the question.

Amy, Eve and Lucy catch different trains to London. Amy's train leaves at 09:45.
Eve's train leaves half an hour after Amy's and arrives in London at 11:15.
Eve's journey takes 15 minutes more than Lucy's. Lucy catches the 11.15 train.
What time does Lucy's train arrive in London? ______________

/1

In the following questions, some words are written in code. The first code in the question has been solved for you. Use the **same** code to work out the second coded word. The alphabet will help you.

A B C D E F G H I J K L M N O P Q R S T U V W X Y Z

Example

If the code for DUCK is EVDL, what is the code for SWAN? TXBO

35. If the code for FORGE is GPSHF, what is the code for RAGE? ________

36. If the code for STEAM is PQBXJ, what is the code for STYLE? ________

37. If the code for POACH is IHTVA, what is the code for GRACE? ________

38. If the code for KNIFE is ILGDC, what does KGLC mean? ________

39. If the code for DAWN is CYTJ, what does RCKZ mean? ________

40. If the code for MOAT is IJUM, what is the code for WISH? ________

41. If the code for SHINE is NMDSZ, what does XWVYZ mean? ________

42. If the code for ABOUT is FWTPY, what does DVBI mean? ________

/8

Find **one** letter that will complete **both** pairs of words, finishing the first word and beginning the second word in each pair. The **same** letter must be used for both pairs of words. Write the letters on the lines provided.

Example

pa (t) ap hi (t)ime

43. as ________ ip fis ________ ot

44. min ________ arn fle ________ eep

45. rea ________ ind roa ________ ipe

46. dre ________ atch cla ________ ary

47. wan ________ ent war ________ awn

48. lea ________ eep soa ________ ilt

49. sla ________ et stor ________ arn

50. mas ________ erb hus ________ eep

/8

In each of the following questions, letters stand for numbers. Work out the answer to each sum. Write your answer as a **letter** on the line provided.

Example

If A = 2, B = 3, C = 4, D = 5, E = 6 and F = 8

what is the answer to this sum written as a letter? D + B = F

If A = 5, B = 7, C = 23, D = 2 and E = 30, what is the value of:

51. $A \times B - E =$ ________

52. $E - C - A =$ ________

53. $B \times A - C - A =$ ________

If A = 8, B = 2, C = 15, D = 3 and E = 20, what is the value of:

54. $C + A - D =$ ________

55. $C \div D + A + B =$ ________

56. $E \div B - D - B + C =$ ________

/6

Change the first word of the third pair in the same way as the other pairs, to give a new word. Write the answers on the lines provided.

Example

tray, dray   tram, dram   trip, drip

57. frill, fill   blend, bend   trail, ________

58. repay, replay   pain, plain   payer, ________

59. have, heave   pace, peace   father, ________

60. planet, plane   comet, come   midget, ________

/4

/60

PAPER 4

On the lines, write the **numbers** that complete each sequence in the most sensible way.

Example

12 14 16 18 20 22

1.	6	____	18	____	30	36		
2.	____	4	____	16	32	64		
3.	2	4	6	10	____	____		
4.	1	4	____	16	25	____		
5.	4	3	6	6	8	9	____	____
6.	6	30	9	25	____	20	15	____
7.	1	2	2	3	____	____	9	14
8.	23	15	19	11	15	7	____	____

/8

In the following questions, move **one** letter from the first word and add it to the second word to make two new words. Do **not** move any other letters. Write **both** new words, which **must make sense**, on the lines provided.

Example

table reed → tale breed

9. chopper hart → ____________ ____________

10. saloon muse → ____________ ____________

11. thread arc → ____________ ____________

12. monkey nave → ____________ ____________

13. feast story → ____________ ____________

14. manager best → ____________ ____________

15. maize minster → ______________ ______________

16. frigid aster → ______________ ______________

/8

In the following sentences, a word of **four letters** is hidden across the **end** of one word and the **start** of the next word. Write the hidden words on the lines provided. The letter order must **not** be changed.

Example

The shop was la**st op**en on Tuesday. stop

17. Catch up with us quickly! ______________

18. We had to climb endless steps to get there. ______________

19. It was so warm all through the day. ______________

20. They are always pleased to see you. ______________

21. What history do you know? ______________

22. His songs often became popular. ______________

/6

Write these words into the grids so that they can each be read across or down.

Example

YET EYE WET MEW AYE MAY

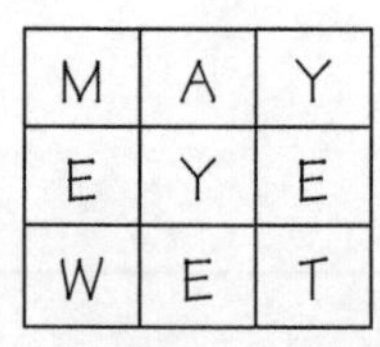

M	A	Y
E	Y	E
W	E	T

23. EVE WAN PEN PEW OVA POP

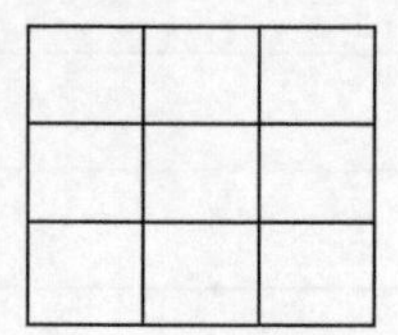

24. TEN ARE PEN ORE TOT TAP

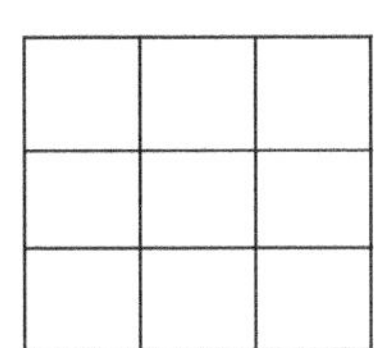

/2

In the following questions, underline the **two** words in each set that are **different** from the others.

Example

potato lemon banana cabbage strawberry

25. scissors	knife	shears	secateurs	fork
26. mouse	keyboard	paper	message	monitor
27. bonnet	shawl	balaclava	cap	cloak
28. shout	hum	yell	scream	whistle
29. synthetic	manmade	natural	organic	artificial
30. vineyard	apples	grapes	orchard	cherries
31. alike	reject	similar	analogous	separate
32. tube	pipe	water	hose	wires

/8

Find the missing **pair of letters** in each sequence. The alphabet has been provided to help you.

A B C D E F G H I J K L M N O P Q R S T U V W X Y Z

Example

MO MK OQ KI QS

33. AD	CF	EH	GJ	IL	______
34. AG	MS	YE	______	WC	
35. CB	FE	IH	LK	______	
36. ZY	XT	SR	NM	LH	______
37. AD	EG	HK	LN	______	
38. WA	VC	UE	______	SI	

/6

In each of the following questions, letters stand for numbers. Work out the answer to each sum. Write your answer as a **letter** on the line provided.

Example

If A = 2, B = 3, C = 4, D = 5, E = 6 and F = 8

what is the answer to this sum written as a letter? D + B = F

If A = 4, B = 3, C = 12, D = 17 and E = 24, what is the value of:

39. A × B + C = ________

40. E − D + C − B − A = ________

41. E ÷ A − B = ________

If V = 5, W = 8, X = 2, Y = 21 and Z = 3, what is the value of:

42. W × X + V = ________

43. Y ÷ Z + W − V − X = ________

44. Z × W − Y = ________

/6

Rearrange all the capital letters to form a correctly spelt word that will complete these sentences sensibly. Write the words on the answer lines.

Example

His pet rabbit was hungry so he fed him a juicy TOCARR. CARROT

45. The TRUNCER was strong and dangerous. ________

46. There were long ESEQUU of traffic in the town. ________

47. The NESSIOPUNS bridge across the gorge was very famous. ________

48. The meteorologist recorded the daily PARRETMEETU. ________

49. Underground they saw the most amazing SLAMGISTATE. ________

50. Each package was carefully BALEDELL. ________

51. The fresh TRICAPOS were delicious. ________

52. She looked it up in the TRYANDICIO. ________

/8

Change the first word of the third pair in the same way as the other pairs, to give a new word. Write the answers on the lines provided.

Example

tray, dray   tram, dram   trip, drip

53. miles, pales   mist, past   mine, ________

54. witch, with   batch, bath   pitch, ________

55. shred, shy   spring, spy   whirl, ________

56. past, step   kale, leek   moth, ________

57. miser, misery   water, watery   flower, ________

58. whist, list   whine, line   whisp, ________

59. mount, ton   fiend, din   faint, ________

/7

Write these words into the grids so that they can each be read across or down.

Example

STEPS   NEEDS   LAPSE   PLAIN   APPLE   POLES

P	O	L	E	S
L		A		T
A	P	P	L	E
I		S		P
N	E	E	D	S

60. HURRY   SILLY   LATER   TOTAL   WILTS   WATCH

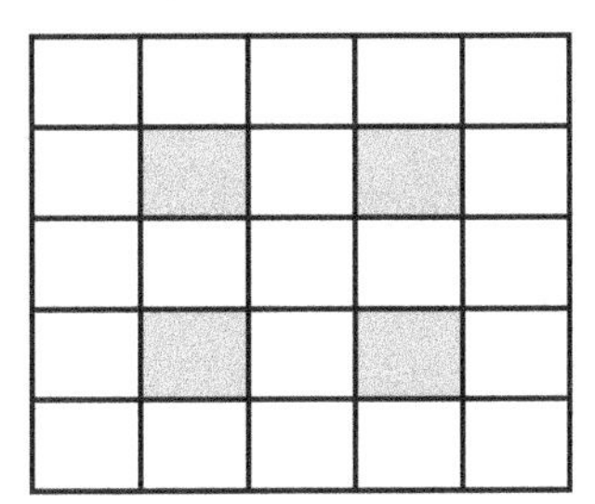

/1

/60

PAPER 5

In the following questions, underline the **two** words, **one** from each set, that have a **similar meaning**.

Example

(car, take, jump) (chair, leap, drive)

1. (marsh, moorland, heather) (heath, bank, park)
2. (petrol, wheels, machine) (tower, engine, crane)
3. (funny, joke, magician) (drama, humorous, tragedy)
4. (pacify, tired, angry) (irrational, irate, biddable)
5. (sausages, fowl, burgers) (poultry, beef, eggs)
6. (newspaper, verse, interview) (prose, essay, rhyme)
7. (rake, spade, trowel) (shovel, fork, hoe)
8. (cable, net, hammock) (fence, wire, stirrup)

/8

In the following questions, underline the **two** words, **one** from each set, that will complete each sentence in the most sensible way.

Example

Head is to (face, arm, neck) as foot is to (leg, knee, thigh).

9. Litter is to (rubbish, puppies, basket) as pride is to (winner, cats, lions).
10. Fear is to (courage, fright, dark) as despair is to (worry, hope, trouble).
11. Fish is to (fingers, cakes, chips) as bread is to (sandwich, butter, loaf).
12. Gale is to (wind, storm, winter) as blizzard is to (white, mountains, snow).
13. Piano is to (tune, key, note) as guitar is to (song, case, string).
14. Tailor is to (sewing, suit, material) as barber is to (hair, scissors, razor).
15. Spring is to (rabbits, autumn, October) as summer is to (August, holidays, winter).
16. Caterpillar is to (cocoon, butterfly, eggs) as tadpole is to (frog, pond, jamjar).

/8

On the lines, write the numbers that complete the sequence in the most sensible way.

Example

4	8	13	19	26	34

17.	6	8	11	15	20	____		
18.	3	6	____	15	21	28		
19.	7	14	14	12	21	____		
20.	21	20	18	15	15	10	____	
21.	13	12	14	13	15	14	16	____
22.	4	9	16	____	36	49		
23.	16	14	15	15	13	16	10	____
24.	2	5	11	23	____	95	191	

/8

Change the first word of the third pair in the same way as the other pairs, to give a new word. Write the answers on the lines provided.

Example

tray, dray   tram, dram   trip, drip

25.	global, lag	petal, lap	bridal, ____________
26.	train, rained	tramp, ramped	trust, ____________
27.	scout, cut	strop, top	cream, ____________
28.	flesh, self	track, cart	steps, ____________
29.	plume, plummet	line, linnet	bone, ____________

/5

In these questions, the word in capitals has had a group of **three** letters taken out. These three letters spell another word, without changing the order. Write the **three-letter** words on the lines provided. The sentences need to make sense.

Example

CABE and beans were her favourite vegetables. BAG

30. Sally was ill and felt MISBLE all day. ________

31. He did some piano PRICE every day. ________

32. The WHER was forecast fair for the camping weekend. ________

33. She was START by the news. ________

34. He could hardly stand because of the damage to his SE. ________

35. They were thrilled to be visiting the exact LOION of the film. ________

36. The archaeologist UNTHED an old coin. ________

37. He quickly mended the fence using the MER. ________

/8

In the following sentences, a word of **four letters** is hidden across the **end** of one word and the **start** of the next word. Write the hidden words on the lines provided. The letter order must **not** be changed.

Example

The shop was la**st op**en on Tuesday. stop

38. Everyone at home was asleep. ________

39. It was a lucky goal in the last minute of the match. ________

40. They also mentioned him by name. ________

41. Each time, a mouse escaped under the door. ________

42. The beach was packed with holidaymakers. ________

43. Please leave my easel over there. ________

44. Moonlight shone brightly on the road ahead. ________

45. That winter coat is too small. ________

/8

46. Visitors at a theme park must be 1.4m tall to go on a rollercoaster.

Danny is the tallest of his group of four friends and he is tall enough to go on the rollercoaster. Chris and Raj are the same height. Tim is taller than Chris but shorter than Danny. Raj is not tall enough to go on the roller coaster.

If these statements are true, only one of the following statements **must** be true. Which one?

A Only Danny could go on the rollercoaster.

B Tim could go on the rollercoaster.

C Chris could not go on the rollercoaster

D Raj is the shortest of the four boys.

E Tim is 1.4m tall. ______________

/1

47. Read the statements below, then answer the question.

Alice, Ben, Maya, Dionne and Tom all belong to a swimming club. Alice goes to swimming training on Mondays, Tuesdays and Thursdays. Ben and Maya also swim on Mondays and Tuesdays but have football practice on Thursday, so they swim on Friday instead. Dionne swims on Tuesdays, Thursdays and Saturdays. Tom trains on Tuesdays, Fridays and Saturdays. The pool is closed on Wednesdays and Sundays.

On which day do all five children swim together? ______________

/1

In each of the following questions, letters stand for numbers. Work out the answer to each sum. Write your answer as a **letter** on the line provided.

Example

If A = 2, B = 3, C = 4, D = 5, E = 6 and F = 8

what is the answer to this sum written as a letter? D + B = F

If A = 4, B = 5, C = 10, D = 2 and E = 19, what is the value of:

48. A × B ÷ D = __________

49. C + A + B = __________

If A = 22, B = 10, C = 2, D = 30 and E = 5, what is the value of:

50. D − A + C = ________

51. D − B + C = ________

52. E × B − D − B = ________

/5

Find **one** letter that will complete **both** pairs of words, finishing the first word and beginning the second word in each pair. The **same** letter must be used for both pairs of words. Write the letters on the lines provided.

Example

pa (t) ap   hi (t)ime

53. mo ________ in   ga ________ ea

54. par ________ elp   for ________ ick

55. hai ________ eap   fee ________ ong

56. bea ________ ack   pou ________ ipe

57. scou ________ une   fea ________ ant

58. nea ________ ine   fla ________ air

59. spur ________ arn   car ________ eam

60. pie ________ ail   stee ________ ock

/8

/60

PAPER 6

Underline the **two** words, **one** from each set, that when put together make one new, correctly spelt word. **The word from the group on the left always comes first.**

Example

(run, use, give) (take, less, red)

1. (con, van, task) (test, pole, rant)
2. (mast, band, vast) (age, ward, let)
3. (hand, hope, bold) (full, some, den)
4. (spin, gain, know) (tip, ledge, less)
5. (swing, in, bold) (chain, spire, den)
6. (in, rat, under) (whey, her, not)
7. (wrap, claw, cap) (port, tor, tour)
8. (nap, toil, bank) (pies, let, nest)

/8

In the first set of three words, the middle word has been made from letters in the other two words. Complete the second set of words in the **same** way to make the missing words, **which must make sense**. Write your answers on the lines provided.

Example

fast (tea) real leaf (fir) hire

9. fence (fleck) clock psalm (__________) waste
10. rash (hear) ware bass (__________) harp
11. paper (creep) peach water (__________) earth
12. rice (pair) pale wasp (__________) clip
13. laser (lease) relax steel (__________) order
14. noble (talon) leant maker (__________) bored

15. video (diver) fried   notes (________) essay

16. crate (utter) trout   grade (________) bread

/8

Find the **relationship** between the **numbers** in the first two sets of brackets. The numbers in the third set of brackets are **related in the same way**. Find the missing number and add it to the final set of brackets.

Example

(6 [48] 8)   (9 [45] 5)   (7 [21] 3)

17. (4 [13] 9)   (11 [23] 12)   (12 [________] 9)

18. (7 [21] 3)   (6 [48] 8)   (4 [________] 12)

19. (9 [3] 3)   (20 [4] 5)   (21 [________] 7)

20. (10 [24] 7)   (2 [18] 8)   (12 [________] 10)

21. (2 [40] 10)   (4 [48] 3)   (6 [________] 2)

22. (72 [18] 8)   (48 [12] 8)   (32 [________] 4)

/6

In these questions, the pairs of letters are **linked** in some way. On the answer lines provided, write the **two** letters that complete the second pair, following the same pattern as the first. The alphabet has been provided to help you.

A B C D E F G H I J K L M N O P Q R S T U V W X Y Z

Example

BY is to **EV** as **HS** is to KP

23. **DF** is to **JL** as **OQ** is to ________

24. **CB** is to **HY** as **JI** is to ________

25. **AB** is to **AG** as **QR** is to ________

26. **WS** is to **UQ** as **PL** is to ________

27. **ZA** is to **XC** as **UF** is to ____________

28. **CY** is to **XT** as **RN** is to ____________

29. **US** is to **SV** as **PN** is to ____________

30. **XC** is to **VE** as **TG** is to ____________

/8

Write these words into the grids so that they can each be read across or down.

Example

YET EYE WET MEW AYE MAY

M	A	Y
E	Y	E
W	E	T

31. NOW EGO TOW MEN MAT AGO

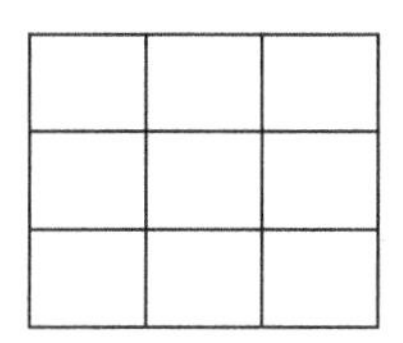

32. APE DUE TAD AMP EMU TEA

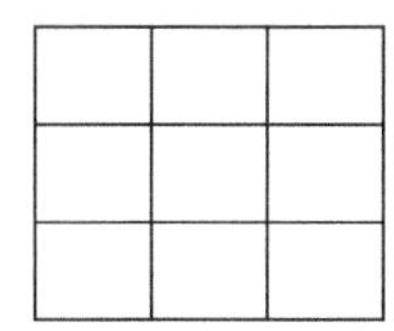

/2

In the following questions, underline the **two** words in each set that are **different** from the others.

Example

potato lemon banana cabbage strawberry

33. unite divide join splice split

34. weep pray sob cry mutter

35. butter	bread	milk	cream	jam
36. run	stroll	saunter	wander	march
37. return	go	arrive	depart	leave
38. smooth	bumpy	regular	uneven	rough
39. grief	sorrow	sanity	sadness	shock
40. rope	wire	string	cord	chain

/8

Find the missing **pair of letters** in each sequence. The alphabet has been provided to help you.

A B C D E F G H I J K L M N O P Q R S T U V W X Y Z

Example

MO MK OQ KI QS

41. OP NQ LS ______ EZ

42. GZ YF EX WD ______

43. TX SW RV ______ PT

44. JI LJ JH NJ JG ______

45. YC ZD AE ______ CG

46. BD AY FH WU JL ______

/6

Change the first word of the **third pair** in the same way as the other pairs, to give a new word. Write the answers on the lines provided.

Example

tray, dray tram, dram trip, drip

47. cater, canter wader, wander cider, ______________

48. strain, stain stroke, stoke string, ______________

49.	wand, winder	lamb, limber	hand, ____________
50.	night, nit	light, lit	sight, ____________
51.	brash, ash	blend, end	stamp, ____________
52.	pot, spots	lit, slits	pin, ____________

/6

Underline the word that **cannot** be made from the letters of the word in capitals.

Example

HANDMADE madden head demand name dream

53.	ENGINEER	grin	green	reign	grain	ring
54.	BEAUTIFUL	felt	table	blue	full	tube
55.	MAGICIAN	nice	icing	manic	gin	main
56.	HELICOPTER	police	tripe	chopper	their	three
57.	WONDERFUL	fund	drone	field	rowed	flower
58.	REINDEER	dine	reed	dinner	erred	rind
59.	MOUNTAIN	main	moat	noun	town	mount
60.	PRESENTED	step	rest	preen	scent	trees

/8

/60

PAPER 7

Find **one** letter that will complete **both** pairs of words, finishing the first word and beginning the second word in each pair. The **same** letter must be used for both pairs of words. Write the letters on the lines provided.

Example

pa (t) ap hi (t)ime

1. ro ________ in fe ________ ar
2. sa ________ od ni ________ ew
3. pos ________ ear plo ________ awn
4. tra ________ ast for ________ ust
5. lac ________ ast lam ________ arn
6. cor ________ are war ________ eat
7. plum ________ arn her ________ rand
8. war ________ own foo ________ rot

/8

Underline **one** word from the list in brackets that goes equally well with both pairs of words outside the brackets.

Example

(ribbon, present, play, theatre, party)

gift, token show, demonstrate

9. (tie, band, choir, ring)
   ensemble, orchestra hoop, strap
10. (sling, rock, sand, clock)
    sway, swing boulder, stone
11. (abrade, score, appraise, tick)
    mark, total groove, cut
12. (elevate, boost, lift, hike)
    hoist, elevator raise, ascend
13. (blockade, bar, stop, block)
    chunk, brick obstruct, hinder
14. (halo, ring, fence, round)
    band, loop enclose, surround
15. (claw, mark, trace, point)
    tip, cusp denote, indicate
16. (duet, match, competition, accord)
    meet, contest couple, pair

/8

In the following questions, move **one** letter from the first word and add it to the second word to make two new words. Do **not** move any other letters. Write **both** new words, which **must make sense**, on the lines provided.

Example

table reed → tale breed

17. folder scar → ______ ______
18. breach heath → ______ ______
19. tracked night → ______ ______
20. whither tent → ______ ______
21. patient clam → ______ ______
22. value pond → ______ ______
23. rapid ounce → ______ ______
24. amiss rely → ______ ______

/8

In these questions, the word in capitals has had a group of **three** letters taken out. These three letters spell another word, without changing the order. Write the **three-letter** words on the lines provided. The sentences need to make sense.

Example

CABE and beans were her favourite vegetables. BAG

25. There was a wonderful smell coming from the CHEN. ______
26. Once the CRS were loaded the removal men drove away. ______
27. The dogs stretched out on the HTH rug. ______
28. They spent a long time REWING the contract. ______
29. She ran the full length of the long COROR. ______
30. It was a SPLEN concert, enjoyed by everyone. ______

31. The policeman applauded the boy for his HSTY. ______________

32. They RCHED for hours trying to find the lost ball. ______________

/8

Underline the word that **cannot** be made from the letters of the word in capitals.

Example

HANDMADE	madden	head	demand	name	<u>dream</u>

33. RELATIVE	later	rivet	trail	river	liver
34. COMMANDER	mean	crane	dome	dream	mound
35. RAILWAY	lair	relay	wail	away	awry
36. FOUNTAIN	faint	noun	nation	tuft	font
37. BALLERINA	baler	liner	brine	aerial	really
38. NAVIGATED	given	dinted	dine	agate	dating
39. AUTOMOBILE	bloom	table	mobile	motor	tomb
40. HOSPITAL	spoil	stop	plate	pith	tails

/8

41. Billy, Hugo, Sam and Kadir want to go bowling together.

A game of bowling costs £4.50 at the weekend and £3.50 during the week.
Billy has £3.20. Hugo has more money than Billy but still not enough to pay for a game of bowling at the weekend. Sam and Kadir could both afford to bowl at the weekend.
If these statements are true, only one of the following statements **must** be true. Which one?

A Sam and Kadir have the same amount of money.

B If they shared their money, all four boys could bowl at the weekend.

C Hugo has the most money of all of the boys.

D If they shared their money, all four boys could bowl during the week.

E Sam has exactly £4.50. ______________

/1

42. Read the statements below, then answer the question.

Lucy's school is east of her home and south of her riding stable.

Her friend Kate lives north of Lucy's home.

These four places form the corners of a square.

Where is Kate's home in relation to the school? ______________

/1

Find the missing **pairs of letters** in the sequence.
The alphabet has been provided to help you.

A B C D E F G H I J K L M N O P Q R S T U V W X Y Z

Example

AD	CF	EH	GJ	IL	KN

43.	FH	KM	______	UW	ZB	______	
44.	HI	KL	NO	______	TU	______	
45.	AC	BD	CE	DF	______	______	
46.	QQ	______	UK	WH	______	AB	CY
47.	YV	WS	TO	______	KD	______	
48.	AA	______	WI	UM	SQ	QU	______
49.	______	FH	IL	MQ	RW	______	
50.	AY	CV	GP	______	UU	______	

/8

Rearrange all the capital letters to form a correctly spelt word that will complete these sentences sensibly. Write the words on the answer lines.

Example

His pet rabbit was hungry so he fed him a juicy TOCARR. CARROT

51. From the NOITUNMA they could see for miles. ______

52. The kittens SCCHATRED the new furniture. ______

53. The ELILETATS beamed back pictures of other planets. ______

54. The crime scene was inspected by the EVICETTED. ______

55. The proud ECCAPKOS strutted about on the lawns. ______

56. They cheered the runners as they watched the HOAMNART. ______

57. Each Christmas, the family went to the HEETTRA. ____________

58. The OURHAT became very popular after his new book. ____________

/8

Write these words into the grids so that they can each be read across or down.

Example

STEPS NEEDS LAPSE PLAIN APPLE POLES

P	O	L	E	S
L		A		T
A	P	P	L	E
I		S		P
N	E	E	D	S

59. DUSTY ENTRY OVERT PASTE STEMS PROUD

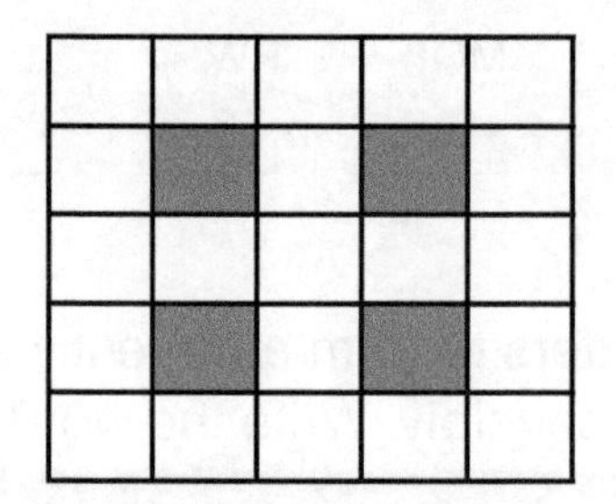

60. DANCE STYLE RAPID CANON ROCKS PANSY

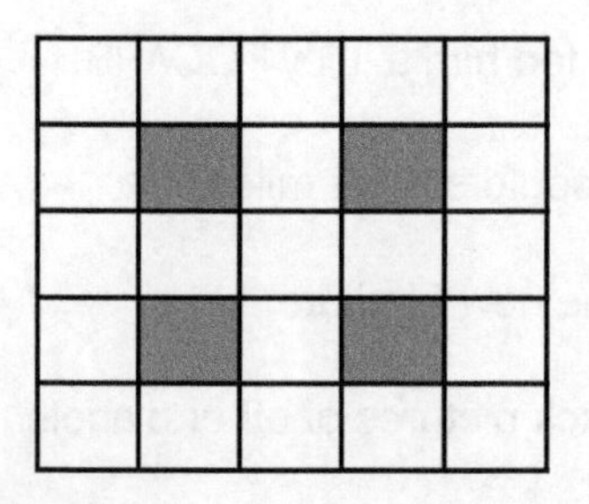

/2

/60

PAPER 8

In the following questions, underline the **two** words, **one** from each set, that have a **similar meaning**.

Example

(car, take, jump) (chair, leap, drive)

1. (probe, prance, practice) (prod, press, precious)
2. (mystery, glory, gleeful) (misery, jovial, smile)
3. (miserable, empty, decadent) (miserly, despondent, deposed)
4. (amputation, actuary, ambition) (recuperation, aspiration, restore)
5. (gallop, woodland, stroll) (flutter, wander, crawl)
6. (push, queue, corner) (shove, exit, alley)
7. (challenge, ask, interview) (reply, complaint, enquire)
8. (swell, waves, manage) (enlarge, reduce, shorten)

/8

In the following questions, underline the **two** words, **one** from each set, that will complete each sentence in the most sensible way.

Example

Head is to (face, arm, neck) as foot is to (leg, knee, thigh).

9. Fish is to (fin, sea, gills) as worm is to (wriggles, bird, earth).
10. Dog is to (bone, lead, kennel) as horse is to (rider, stable, saddle).
11. Pastry is to (apple, pie, golden) as bread is to (sandwich, bakery, loaf).
12. Cow is to (roast, beef, milk) as sheep is to (shepherd, chops, mutton).
13. Thesaurus is to (translation, synonyms, alphabet) as dictionary is to (lexicon, definitions, glossary).
14. Hot is to (oven, bake, sun) as cold is to (ice, winter, fridge).

/6

These four words have been written as **number codes**, but one of the codes is missing. The words and codes are not necessarily in the same order. Write the answers to the questions on the lines provided.

STABLE BLEATS TABLET BEASTS

165341 534612 216534

15. Pick out the code for STABLE. ____________

16. Pick out the word with the number code 165341. ____________

17. Which word is missing a code? ____________

18. What is the code for the word in answer 17? ____________

DROOP PRODS SPORE PEERS

46235 36224 54261

19. Pick out the code for SPORE. ____________

20. Pick out the word with the number code 46235. ____________

21. Which word is missing a code? ____________

22. What would be the code for ROPED? ____________

/8

In the first set of three words, the middle word has been made from letters in the other two words. Complete the second set of words in the **same** way to make the missing words, **which must make sense**. Write your answers on the lines provided.

Example

fast (tea) real leaf (fir) hire

23. flop (loaf) fail bled (____________) paid

24. mare (harm) shoe real (____________) spin

25. scout (uncut) uncle spire (____________) tours

26. claim (calm) meant slick (__________) yearn

27. roast (steer) revel grate (__________) smear

28. meant (name) gnome arrow (__________) swoop

29. raise (rates) stare sleep (__________) coast

30. faint (final) flake spray (__________) gears

/8

In the following questions, some words are written in code. The first code in the question has been solved for you. Use the **same** code to work out the second coded word. The alphabet will help you.

A B C D E F G H I J K L M N O P Q R S T U V W X Y Z

Example

If the code for DUCK is EVDL, what is the code for SWAN? TXBO

31. If the code for FOAL is DMYJ, what is the code for LOAN? __________

32. If the code for BLIND is WGDIY, what is the code for BLOAT? __________

33. If the code for GRAPE is IUEUK, what is the code for SOUND? __________

34. If the code for WINDY is COTJE, what does HGTPU mean? __________

35. If the code for PIECE is BUQOQ, what does RAGZP mean? __________

36. If the code for CREST is YNAOP, what is the code for BLAME? __________

37. If the code for RAISIN is PXENCG, what does EOKVHL mean? __________

38. If the code for MOULD is HSRNC, what does BVBGM mean? __________

/8

To complete these questions, you need to **balance** the **numbers** on each side of the equation. Start by working out the calculation on the left. Next, find the missing number that will give the same total on the right-hand side.

Example

$10 \times 6 \div 5 = 22 + 3 - [13]$

39. $(12 + 7) - 11 = (7 + \_\_\_\_) - 4$

40. $6 \times 8 \div 12 = 3 \times 5 - \_\_\_\_$

41. $\frac{(12 \times 2)}{3} = \frac{(16 \times 2)}{\_\_\_\_}$

42. $4(3 + 4) = (60 \div 2) - \_\_\_\_$

43. $2\frac{(4 \times 5)}{4} = \frac{(6 \times \_\_\_\_)}{3}$

44. $\frac{(15 \times 4)}{5} = 3 + \_\_\_\_$

/6

Change the first word of the third pair in the same way as the other pairs, to give a new word. Write the answers on the lines provided.

Example

tray, dray   tram, dram   trip, drip

45. male, meal   tare, tear   lane, ____________

46. ashen, she   brand, ran   grime, ____________

47. medal, metal   plead, pleat   drip, ____________

48. chick, hid   wreck, red   trick, ____________

49. babble, bale   dabble, dale   rubble, ____________

50. celebration, celebrate   notation, notate   congregation, ____________

/6

Underline the word that **cannot** be made from the letters of the word in capitals.

Example

HANDMADE	madden	head	demand	name	dream

(dream is underlined in the example)

51. STRANDED	sand	read	drain	trade	dared
52. MISSILE	lime	miss	slim	mile	mail
53. RESTAURANT	truant	treat	stare	trust	struts
54. WRESTLER	reset	were	slew	wrist	steer
55. MINIATURE	nature	train	manure	triune	trump

/5

In each of the following questions, letters stand for numbers. Work out the answer to each sum. Write your answer as a **letter** on the line provided.

Example

If A = 2, B = 3, C = 4, D = 5, E = 6 and F = 8

what is the answer to this sum written as a letter? D + B = F

If A = 4, B = 6, C = 16, D = 32 and E = 2, what is the value of:

56. A × B + E + B = ________

57. D ÷ A + B + C + E = ________

If A = 25, B = 7, C = 3, D = 40 and E = 6, what is the value of:

58. C × E + B = ________

59. D − A − E − C = ________

60. C × B + A − E = ________

/5

/60

PAPER 9

Find the **relationship** between the **numbers** in the first two sets of brackets. The numbers in the third set of brackets are **related in the same way**. Find the missing number and add it to the final set of brackets.

Example

(6 [48] 8) (9 [45] 5) (7 [21] 3)

1. (11 [8] 3) (23 [17] 6) (27 [____] 9)
2. (6 [48] 8) (3 [27] 9) (8 [____] 7)
3. (49 [7] 7) (28 [7] 4) (48 [____] 8)
4. (3 [10] 1) (6 [38] 2) (9 [____] 11)
5. (15 [7] 3) (16 [6] 4) (48 [____] 6)
6. (2 [13] 3) (1 [17] 4) (5 [____] 4)
7. (3 [36] 6) (2 [28] 7) (5 [____] 6)

/7

In the following questions, underline the **two** words, **one** from each set, that will complete each sentence in the most sensible way.

Example

Head is to (face, arm, neck) as foot is to (leg, knee, thigh).

8. Wheat is to (bread, fields, straw) as grass is to (bale, hay, winter).
9. Foot is to (sock, toes, sole) as hand is to (palm, ring, knuckle).
10. Digits are to (tables, numbers, problems) as letters are to (calligraphy, post, words).
11. Stem is to (green, bud, flower) as trunk is to (branch, tree, wood).
12. Doctor is to (medicine, surgery, patient) as lawyer is to (judge, client, papers).
13. Elements are to (science, chemistry, school) as forces are to (physics, space, gravity).
14. Cross is to (sign, mark, wrong) as tick is to (insect, correct, sheep).
15. Red is to (wine, stop, danger) as green is to (grass, nature, go).

/8

Underline the **two** words, **one** from each set, that when put together make one new, correctly spelt word. **The word from the group on the left always comes first.**

Example

(run, use, give) (take, less, red)

16. (roll, leaf, draw) (let, front, pot)
17. (post, tie, hole) (are, age, lace)
18. (din, scar, ink) (let, age, lore)
19. (bet, hot, lag) (ray, ten, for)
20. (cap, opt, way) (ion, don, par)
21. (bow, flea, pop) (led, era, sty)
22. (led, ban, car) (stay, ring, away)
23. (fort, sly, seal) (horse, ant, bird)

/8

In the following sentences, a word of **four letters** is hidden across the **end** of one word and the **start** of the next word. Write the hidden words on the lines provided. The letter order must **not** be changed.

Example

The shop was la**st op**en on Tuesday. stop

24. Carrying the baggage was tiring. ______
25. Shall we go all round the town? ______
26. She chose peach and strawberry ice-cream. ______
27. She took the skipping rope as we left the house. ______
28. Please amend this letter today. ______
29. Camping out was such fun! ______

30. The bear chose to sleep in the tree. ______________

31. It is what everyone likes. ______________

/8

Write these words into the grids so that they can each be read across or down.

Example

YET EYE WET MEW AYE MAY

M	A	Y
E	Y	E
W	E	T

32. TAT EAT ATE PEA APT TEA

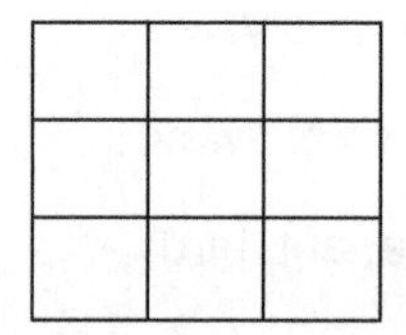

33. NEW OVA EVE CEP CON PAW

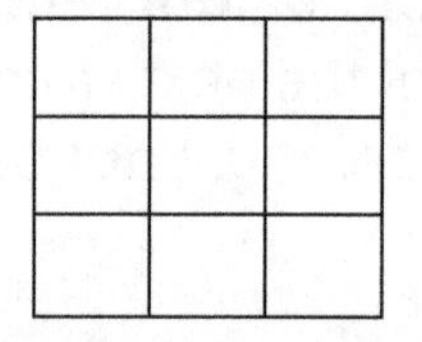

/2

In the following questions, underline the **two** words in each set that are **different** from the others.

Example

potato lemon banana cabbage strawberry

(In the example, "potato" and "cabbage" are underlined.)

34. shed garage chalet lodge mansion

35. dependable variable unpredictable trustworthy reliable

36. weaken fade mature lessen increase

37. price money value cost merit

38.	cottage	yoghurt	Cheddar	Brie	grated
39.	spade	wheelbarrow	fork	trowel	bucket

/6

Change the first word of the third pair in the same way as the other pairs, to give a new word. Write the answers on the lines provided.

Example

tray, dray   tram, dram   trip, drip

40. man, manage   post, postage   pilgrim, ____________

41. western, wet   venture, vet   hostage, ____________

42. tar, stare   lop, slope   car, ____________

43. plain, pan   spilt, sit   cramp, ____________

44. western, wry   natural, nay   concern, ____________

45. match, tame   ditch, tide   patch, ____________

46. count, nut   front, not   kilt, ____________

/7

Find **one** letter that will complete **both** pairs of words, finishing the first word and beginning the second word in each pair. The **same** letter must be used for both pairs of words. Write the letters on the lines provided.

Example

pa (t) ap   hi (t)ime

47. hi ________ oy   ar ________ in

48. lea ________ ail   loa ________ ace

49. tal ________ ick   rac ________ een

50. fea ________ est   bea ________ alk

51. grow ________ one   grai ________ orth

52. nai ________ ist foa ________ and

53. mea ________ ear dar ________ orm

54. lam ________ each sla ________ arn

/8

Underline the word that **cannot** be made from the letters of the word in capitals.

Example

HANDMADE	madden	head	demand	name	dream
55. PAGEANT	pent	tang	agent	gauge	page
56. CHAMPION	pinch	camp	niche	chimp	moan
57. MONARCHY	arch	roan	charm	army	marry
58. WITNESS	stint	tins	wines	newt	swine
59. MESMERISE	simmer	miser	seer	mimes	reams
60. BLANKET	belt	talker	bank	table	bleak

/6

/60

PAPER 10

In the following questions, underline the **two** words, **one** from each set, that have a **similar meaning**.

Example

(car, take, jump) (chair, leap, drive)

1. (voices, unison, chorus) (prohibited, refrain, musical)
2. (sleaze, slip, slothful) (slight, slender, slither)
3. (brush, bristle, vacuum) (break, carpet, sweep)
4. (commute, argue, cooperate) (berate, collaborate, castigate)
5. (present, conceal, exhibit) (exposure, display, prevent)
6. (dresser, desk, chest) (piano, bureau, mannequin)
7. (threaten, dangerous, scared) (intimidate, horrible, pretend)
8. (possession, relation, cherish) (value, provision, vanity)

/8

Underline **one** word from the list in brackets that goes equally well with both pairs of words outside the brackets.

Example

(ribbon, present, play, theatre, party)

gift, token show, demonstrate

9. (glint, stick, lean, curve)
   tilt, incline thin, gaunt
10. (grab, clutch, grasp, catch)
   capture, ensnare clasp, hook
11. (crop, produce, make, goods)
   yield, harvest direct, perform
12. (cabinet, board, strip, conclave)
   committee, panel plank, slat
13. (exhaust, collapse, crumple, break)
   pause, rest smash, shatter
14. (beat, hose, tap, swat)
   rap, strike nozzle, spout
15. (ring, lap, lash, droop)
   lick, drink loop, circuit
16. (jetty, cover, cape, ness)
   headland, peninsula cloak, coat

/8

In the following questions, move **one** letter from the first word and add it to the second word to make two new words. Do **not** move any other letters. Write **both** new words, which **must make sense**, on the lines provided.

Example

table reed → tale breed

17. jocular argon → ________ ________

18. preview sender → ________ ________

19. cream sale → ________ ________

20. thrice treat → ________ ________

21. reveal forge → ________ ________

22. wrinkle fail → ________ ________

23. planet naive → ________ ________

24. factor unction → ________ ________

/8

In these questions, the pairs of letters are **linked** in some way. On the answer lines provided, write the **two** letters that complete the second pair, following the same pattern as the first. The alphabet has been provided to help you.

A B C D E F G H I J K L M N O P Q R S T U V W X Y Z

Example

BY is to **EV** as **HS** is to KP

25. **EF** is to **EG** as **MN** is to ________

26. **JG** is to **NK** as **RO** is to ________

27. **AF** is to **JH** as **QV** is to ________

28. **PI** is to **NU** as **BU** is to ________

29. **ZW** is to **WU** as **PM** is to ______

30. **BY** is to **DW** as **FU** is to ______

31. **VX** is to **SN** as **RT** is to ______

32. **WU** is to **TR** as **MK** is to ______

/8

In the following questions, underline the **two** words in each set that are **different** from the others.

Example

potato lemon banana cabbage strawberry

33. eagle	moorhen	chicken	duck	swan
34. snack	breakfast	dinner	banquet	supper
35. clock	barometer	watch	chronometer	candle
36. detain	discard	reject	invite	decline
37. clam	slug	squid	mussel	limpet
38. courage	fear	bravery	battle	valour
39. pen	rubber	biro	pencil	ruler
40. fountain	volcano	waterfall	rapids	cave

/8

Change the first word of the third pair in the same way as the other pairs, to give a new word. Write the answers on the lines provided.

Example

tray, dray tram, dram trip, drip

41. crown, drown	cone, done	cream, ______
42. bottle, bet	waddle, wed	riddle, ______
43. pall, poll	warm, worm	mare, ______
44. bunch, bush	winch, wish	ranch, ______
45. node, den	wane, new	tape, ______
46. top, stopper	lip, slipper	pot, ______

/6

In each of the following questions, letters stand for numbers. Work out the answer to each sum. Write your answer as a **letter** on the line provided.

Example

If A = 2, B = 3, C = 4, D = 5, E = 6 and F = 8

what is the answer to this sum written as a letter? D + B = F

If A = 5, B = 7, C = 12, D = 2 and E = 22, what is the value of:

47. A + B + C − E = ________

48. A × D + C = ________

49. E + D − C = ________

If A = 30, B = 25, C = 5, D = 2 and E = 50, what is the value of:

50. E ÷ D + C = ________

51. C × D + E − A = ________

52. E − A + C = ________

/6

The last word can be formed from the first word by changing three letters. Each letter-change creates a correctly spelt word. Write in the missing words in the spaces provided. The order of the letters does not change.

Example

SWAN swam swim SLIM

53. MIND ________ ________ DONE

54. COLT ________ ________ BOAR

55. BEAR ________ ________ SEED

56. WIRE ________ ________ WAND

57. STOP ________ ________ WHIP

58. BIRD ________ ________ BONE

59. DONE ________ ________ CAPE

60. BULB ________ ________ CALL

/8

/60

PAPER 11

In the following questions, underline the **two** words, **one** from each set, that are **opposite in meaning**.

Example

(talk, run, whisper) (sprint, shout, speak)

1.	(arrive, reach, attain)	(desist, leave, rely)
2.	(decide, forego, commence)	(condense, conclude, conspire)
3.	(misuse, ruin, squander)	(collect, hoard, arrange)
4.	(nearly, biased, all)	(partial, fair, sum)
5.	(forward, provide, advance)	(receive, retreat, hesitate)
6.	(require, notice, request)	(ignore, irate, follow)

/6

These four words have been written as **number codes**, but one of the codes is missing. The words and codes are not necessarily in the same order. Write the answers to the questions on the lines provided.

RISES	VERSE	SERVE	SIEVE
46151	41251	51241	

7. Pick out the code for SIEVE. __________

8. Pick out the word with the number code 51241. __________

9. Which word is missing a code? __________

10. What is the code for the word in answer 9? __________

TALLER	RETIRE	TILLER	RETAIL
362251	342251	153462	

11. Pick out the code for TILLER. __________

12. Pick out the word with the number code 153462. __________

13. Which word is missing a code? ____________

14. What would be the code for RELATE? ____________

/8

In the following questions, underline the **two** words, **one** from each set, that will complete each sentence in the most sensible way.

Example

Head is to (face, arm, neck) as foot is to (leg, knee, thigh).

15. Mine is to (shaft, coal, dark) as well is to (water, bucket, wet).
16. Right is to (turn, correct, left) as forward is to (straight, reverse, ahead).
17. King is to (crown, queen, monarch) as count is to (countess, princess, marquis).
18. Owl is to (predator, mouse, night) as lark is to (day, feather, song).
19. Dawn is to (sunrise, dusk, early) as morning is to (day, breakfast, evening).
20. Choir is to (school, voices, songs) as orchestra is to (instruments, concert, drums).

/6

In these questions, the word in capitals has had a group of **three** letters taken out. These three letters spell another word, without changing the order. Write the **three-letter** words on the lines provided. The sentences need to make sense.

Example

CABE and beans were her favourite vegetables. BAG

21. The children took turns to play games on the COMER. ____________
22. The family suffered another TEDY. ____________
23. The false rumours and ALATIONS were upsetting. ____________
24. The climbers wore special TMAL clothing. ____________
25. They were learning about reptiles in BIOY lessons. ____________
26. He spoke in a very quiet WPER. ____________
27. The band played a lively MH. ____________
28. The orchestra gave a wonderful PERMANCE. ____________

/8

In the following sentences, a word of **four letters** is hidden across the **end** of one word and the **start** of the next word. Write the hidden words on the lines provided. The letter order must **not** be changed.

Example

The shop was la**st op**en on Tuesday. _stop_

29. Please wash and put the things away. ________

30. This is the best ankle support you can have. ________

31. Everything is explained in the attached letter. ________

32. A good story has to end happily ever after. ________

33. While approaching the gate, he heard the dog bark. ________

34. The swan gracefully swam past our barge. ________

35. The fields were surrounded with fences and hedges. ________

36. The porcupine stole the dog's food. ________

/8

37. On sports day Trudy, Max, Laura and Gina try to beat the school long jump record by jumping more than 2.5 metres.

Trudy jumps 2.3 metres. Laura jumps 2.7 metres. Both Gina and Max jump further than Trudy.

If these statements are true, only one of the following statements **must** be true. Which one?

A Laura sets a new school long jump record.

B Gina and Max jump further than Laura.

C Only Trudy fails to break the school record.

D Laura, Gina and Max all break the school record.

E The school long jump record is broken on sports day. ________

/1

38. Read the statements below, then answer the question.

Chris, Ryan, Molly and Emma all play football.

Molly and Emma play netball. Ryan plays rugby and cricket.

Chris plays basketball and squash.

Emma and Chris play hockey.

Who plays the most sports? ____________

/1

Find the missing **pair of letters** in each sequence.
has been provided to help you.

A B C D E F G H I J K L M N O P Q R S T U V W X Y Z

Example

MO MK OQ KI QS

39. BD EG HJ ______

40. XV RT PN JL ______

41. ZA VE RI ______ JQ

42. GH FE KL DC OP ______

43. XL WM YK VN ______

44. ZY XV UR QM ______

/6

Rearrange all the capital letters to form a correctly spelt word that will complete these sentences sensibly. Write the words on the answer lines.

Example

His pet rabbit was hungry so he fed him a juicy TOCARR. CARROT

45. The books were arranged in ETALPICAHABL order. ____________

46. The REERRVOSI was in a national park. ____________

47. It was dark and quiet in the middle of the STROFE. ____________

48. The CHOIRST is a very fast bird. ____________

49. They waited for hours in the REAPTRUDE lounge. ____________

50. They had a special meal in the new TARTSURENA. ____________

/6

Find **one** letter that will complete **both** pairs of words, finishing the first word and beginning the second word in each pair. The **same** letter must be used for both pairs of words. Write the letters on the lines provided.

Example

pa (t) ap hi (t)ime

51. ski ______ oon bea ______ ean

52. gri ______ ake war ______ our

53. grou ______ ear sor ______ ore

54. star ______ mit lam ______ lope

/4

In the following questions, underline the **two** words, **one** from each set, that have a **similar meaning**.

Example

(car, take, jump) (chair, leap, drive)

55. (worried, quiet, single) (pensioner, alone, refugee)

56. (fierce, strong, courageous) (tall, ferocious, coward)

57. (bank, ditch, yard) (hedge, slope, square)

58. (star, Earth, galaxy) (meteor, moon, globe)

59. (quarrel, friend, grumpy) (argument, cousin, discussion)

60. (nation, river, ocean) (continent, country, lake)

/6

/60

PAPER 12

The last word can be formed from the first word by changing three letters. Each letter-change creates a correctly spelt word. Write in the missing words in the spaces provided. The order of the letters does not change.

Example

SWAN _swam_ _swim_ SLIM

1. MINK ______ ______ TINY
2. PINE ______ ______ FOND
3. ROPE ______ ______ RISK
4. DAMP ______ ______ MIME
5. VEST ______ ______ BEND
6. HILL ______ ______ PULP

/6

In the following questions, underline the **two** words, **one** from each set, that will complete each sentence in the most sensible way.

Example

Head is to (face, arm, neck) as foot is to (leg, knee, thigh).

7. Fall is to (trip, rise, drop) as descend is to (lift, escalator, ascend).
8. Funny is to (comedy, laugh, joke) as sad is to (accident, tragedy, theatre).
9. Wine is to (grapes, cork, bottle) as jam is to (tea, jar, sandwich).
10. Bird is to (flying, twitter, nest) as squirrel is to (drey, nuts, tail).
11. Ruby is to (ring, stone, red) as emerald is to (green, grass, sparkle).
12. Beginning is to (preface, chapter, end) as introduction is to (conclusion, index, blurb).

/6

Underline the **two** words, **one** from each set, that when put together make one new, correctly spelt word. **The word from the group on the left always comes first**.

Example

(run, use, give) (take, less, red)

13. (rest, win, port) (ray, form, lock)

14. (live, shop, ray) (lea, stock, bow)

15. (plain, raw, sea) (ton, side, den)

16. (bar, bit, mist) (ten, tor, rain)

17. (ray, fork, wit) (son, her, ton)

18. (sea, let, more) (lack, son, ore)

19. (can, won, not) (ice, let, her)

20. (wind, sun, gloss) (dry, wave, row)

/8

Write these words into the grids so that they can each be read across or down.

Example

YET EYE WET MEW AYE MAY

M	A	Y
E	Y	E
W	E	T

21. ORE WET NET ARE CAN COW

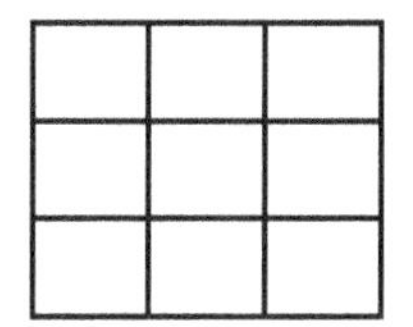

22. DEW NEW ICE ACE BAN BID

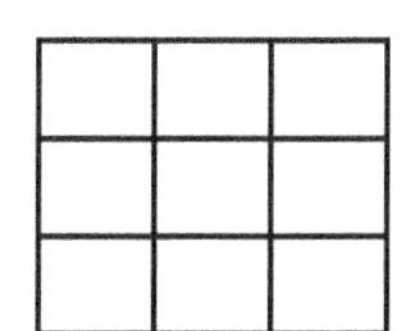

/2

In the following questions, underline the **two** words in each set that are **different** from the others.

Example

potato lemon banana cabbage strawberry

23.	plantation	desert	orchard	farm	wilderness
24.	dark	daylight	nocturnal	hibernating	night
25.	canter	skip	gallop	trot	tiptoe
26.	teach	learn	instruct	coach	follow
27.	diameter	circumference	edge	radius	height
28.	lettuce	carrots	cabbage	parsley	rhubarb
29.	valuable	ancient	rare	old	antique
30.	valley	peak	glen	dale	ridge

/8

Find the missing **pairs of letters** in the sequence. The alphabet has been provided to help you.

A B C D E F G H I J K L M N O P Q R S T U V W X Y Z

Example

AD CF EH GJ IL KN

31.	BC	EF	HI	KL	____	____	
32.	CE	DG	FJ	____	MS	____	
33.	____	VS	RO	NK	____	FC	
34.	MN	OL	KP	QJ	IR	____	____
35.	____	FH	IK	LN	OQ	____	
36.	FC	____	BY	ZW	XU	____	
37.	____	TM	VK	XI	____	BE	
38.	____	AX	BW	CV	____	ET	

/8

On the lines, write the numbers that complete the sequence in the most sensible way.

Example

12	14	16	18	20	22

39.	9	12	_____	18	21	_____
40.	8	12	16	_____	_____	28
41.	4	8	16	_____	64	_____
42.	1	4	9	16	_____	_____
43.	_____	4	6	_____	16	26
44.	_____	18	20	_____	22	6
45.	28	6	_____	9	14	_____
46.	3	_____	15	31	_____	127

/8

These four words have been written as **number codes**, but one of the codes is missing. The words and codes are not necessarily in the same order. Write the answers to the questions on the lines provided.

TRUTH	THORN	TROUT	NORTH
24512	65423	24123	

47. Pick out the code for TRUTH. _______________

48. Pick out the word with the number code 65423. _______________

49. Which word is missing a code? _______________

50. What is the code for the word in answer 49? _______________

SLAPS	PLATE	STEAL	LEAPS
21356	41324	16324	

51. Pick out the code for PLATE. _______________

52. Pick out the word with the number code 41324. _______________

53. Which word is missing a code? ____________

54. What would be the code for PLEATS? ____________

/8

Underline the word that **cannot** be made from the letters of the word in capitals.

Example

HANDMADE	madden	head	demand	name	dream

55. COTTAGE	coat	cage	gout	tact	tote
56. UNIVERSITY	vine	serve	unity	stir	stern
57. PALATIAL	till	pall	plait	pilau	lilt
58. BEDSPREAD	bread	spear	dread	bears	pride
59. NEWSPAPER	swap	paws	panes	pawn	wines
60. COMPUTER	crop	cure	rump	coat	trump

/6

/60

PAPER 13

In the following questions, underline the **two** words, **one** from each set, that have a **similar meaning**.

Example

(car, take, jump) (chair, leap, drive)

1. (angel, heaven, painting) (halo, cherub, trumpet)
2. (flourish, hold, sheath) (flamboyant, brandish, surreptitious)
3. (bandage, wound, accident) (injure, fatality, stretcher)
4. (stretch, coil, elastic) (flatten, compress, extend)
5. (return, parachute, flee) (safari, escape, journey)
6. (interesting, question, interruption) (questionnaire, interrogate, interpret)
7. (notorious, famous, reputation) (fanatic, promotion, eminent)
8. (reward, gold, ransom) (reality, recompense, famous)

/8

In the following questions, underline the **two** words, **one** from each set, that will complete each sentence in the most sensible way.

Example

Head is to (face, arm, neck) as foot is to (leg, knee, thigh).

9. Weight is to (kilograms, scales, lead) as temperature is to (thermometer, hot, fever).
10. Wool is to (knitting, sheep, jumpers) as cotton is to (wool, sewing, needle).
11. Old is to (antique, ancient, young) as age is to (youth, birthday, years).
12. Prince is to (fairytale, princess, royalty) as duke is to (countess, lady, duchess).
13. Sheep are to (flock, herd, pack) as wolves are to (group, pack, coven).
14. Clutch is to (hens, cars, eggs) as school is to (teachers, fish, lessons).
15. Carpenter is to (hammer, wood, nails) as blacksmith is to (horseshoe, forge, metal).
16. Mouse is to (cheese, trap, cat) as dog is to (lead, walk, bone).

/8

In the following questions, move **one** letter from the first word and add it to the second word to make two new words. Do **not** move any other letters. Write **both** new words, which **must make sense**, on the lines provided.

Example

table reed → *tale* *breed*

17. crown pedant → ______ ______
18. crockery inset → ______ ______
19. moat taster → ______ ______
20. budget sage → ______ ______
21. thread was → ______ ______
22. grouse liner → ______ ______
23. dream sever → ______ ______
24. starve beet → ______ ______

/8

These four words have been written as **number codes**, but one of the codes is missing. The words and codes are not necessarily in the same order. Write the answers to the questions on the lines provided.

RIVERS	REVIVE	STREET	STEERS
562235	563226	321412	

25. Pick out the code for STREET. ______
26. Pick out the word with the number code 321412. ______
27. Which word is missing a code? ______
28. What is the code for the word in answer 27? ______

TIME	MINT	PINE	PINT
6152	4153	6153	

29. Pick out the code for PINE. ______
30. Pick out the word with the number code 6153. ______

31. Which word is missing a code? ______________

32. What would be the code for TENT? ______________

/8

In these questions, the word in capitals has had a group of **three** letters taken out. These three letters spell another word, without changing the order. Write the **three-letter** words on the lines provided. The sentences need to make sense.

Example

CABE and beans were her favourite vegetables. BAG

33. The rich family lived in an amazing SION. ______________

34. The family left the house before the HURRIE struck. ______________

35. There was enough MRIAL to make a pair of curtains. ______________

36. The BER cut his hair too short. ______________

37. The SHEPD went everywhere with his dogs. ______________

38. It took several hours for the large KER to turn around. ______________

39. In the cathedral, each DOW told a story. ______________

40. The extinct volcano had left an enormous CER. ______________

/8

41. Charlie, Megan and Dan agree to meet at the cinema at 6.30pm to watch a film which starts at 6.40pm.

Megan and Dan both arrive before Charlie.

Charlie arrives at 6.50pm.

If these statements are true, only one of the following statements **must** be true. Which one?

A Megan and Dan arrive together.

B Dan arrives on time.

C Megan arrives between 6.30 and 6.40.

D Charlie misses the start of the film.

E All of the friends miss the start of the film. ______________

/1

42. Read the statements below, then answer the question.

Schoolchildren analyse the running times of the first and last runners to cross the finish line in a fun run.

The fastest runner completes the course in 45 minutes.

The slowest runner takes twice as long to complete the race.

The race began at 10.30am but the slowest runner arrived at the start line late and began 10 minutes later.

At what time did the slowest runner cross the finish line? ______________

/1

Rearrange all the capital letters to form a correctly spelt word that will complete these sentences sensibly. Write the words on the answer lines.

Example

His pet rabbit was hungry so he fed him a juicy TOCARR. CARROT

43. She looked in her BEADROWR to find the red dress. ______________

44. Folding and putting each leaflet in an PEELOVEN took a long time! ______________

45. The YEDSKON on the beach were well cared for. ______________

46. They decided to enter the INEPTMOOTIC. ______________

47. He inspected the GNATIVE car carefully. ______________

48. They ate SANDCOYFLS as they walked around the fair. ______________

49. She made an EEETOMTL with the eggs. ______________

50. The wedding card said ARTGUNICOONSALT. ______________

/8

In each of the following questions, letters stand for numbers. Work out the answer to each sum. Write your answer as a **letter** on the line provided.

Example

If A = 2, B = 3, C = 4, D = 5, E = 6 and F = 8

what is the answer to this sum written as a letter? D + B = F

If A = 16, B = 20, C = 3, D = 5 and E = 7, what is the value of:

51. B ÷ D + C = ________

52. C × E − A = ________

53. E − C + A = ________

If A = 5, B = 2, C = 10, D = 25 and E = 15, what is the value of:

54. B × D ÷ A = ________

55. A × C − D − E = ________

56. C ÷ B + A = ________

/6

Underline the word that **can** be made from the letters of the word in capitals.

Example

CRUSADER	crude	rush	pears	raider	dress

57. COMPETITION	compost	impact	cotton	common	minute
58. TRANSVERSE	severe	vestry	reason	every	ravens
59. GEOMETRY	gnome	metre	energy	comet	timer
60. MAGNETIC	timing	magic	menace	entice	icing

/4

/60

PAPER 14

In the following questions, underline the **two** words, **one** from each set, that are **opposite in meaning**.

Example

(talk, run, whisper) (sprint, shout, speak)

1. (green, modern, fresh) (dry, gone, stale)
2. (brandish, banish, unfair) (welcome, bond, establish)
3. (precocious, premonition, precarious) (dubious, stable, destroyed)
4. (delight, inform, favour) (insult, betray, disappoint)
5. (expulsion, relaxation, elation) (deflation, refer, despair)
6. (sought, slight, weary) (stocky, partial, whole)
7. (refuse, attached, secure) (reject, uncertain, choose)
8. (argue, condemn, excuse) (pardon, repeat, refrain)

/8

Underline the **two** words, **one** from each set, that when put together make one new, correctly spelt word. **The word from the group on the left always comes first.**

Example

(run, use, give) (take, less, red)

9. (band, cow, more) (wing, age, ore)
10. (scare, bit, bar) (doe, low, crow)
11. (bee, but, sit) (ring, ton, lore)
12. (loss, tray, bar) (lore, ness, gain)
13. (are, nest, swing) (led, shore, let)
14. (two, twin, tat) (tore, too, tor)
15. (sun, rum, fill) (bled, fore, ban)
16. (floor, tea, test) (ring, tor, mesh)

/8

In the first set of three words, the middle word has been made from letters in the other two words. Complete the second set of words in the **same** way to make the missing words, **which must make sense**. Write your answers on the lines provided.

Example

fast (tea) real — leaf (fir) hire

17. dish (bash) band — type (________) hole
18. wand (wait) bait — hind (________) foot
19. stamp (palm) pale — going (________) hair
20. birch (hire) chore — bendy (________) start
21. gable (bulge) gully — label (________) wrath
22. glaze (wear) rower — spilt (________) laser
23. build (load) board — swell (________) learn
24. glory (gear) anger — lanky (________) angel

/8

In the following sentences, a word of **four letters** is hidden across the **end** of one word and the **start** of the next word. Write the hidden words on the lines provided. The letter order must **not** be changed.

Example

The shop was la**st op**en on Tuesday. — stop

25. Most ripe fruit will attract wasps. ________
26. They turned the car park into a market. ________
27. Please fasten the seat belt. ________
28. It was a tip inside the house. ________
29. The weasel found a way out of the cage. ________
30. The drum played loudly during the last march. ________

31. The child was pushed aside. ________

32. The predator ate the fish quickly. ________

/8

On the lines, write the numbers that complete the sequence in the most sensible way.

Example

4 8 13 19 26 34

33.	6	12	18	24	____	36
34.	1	2	3	5	8	____
35.	81	64	49	36	____	16
36.	48	43	38	33	____	23
37.	2	4	3	9	____	16
38.	1	1	2	4	7	____
39.	4	7	8	____	16	21
40.	33	24	____	18	21	12

/8

Find the missing **pair of letters** in each sequence. The alphabet has been provided to help you.

A B C D E F G H I J K L M N O P Q R S T U V W X Y Z

Example

MO MK OQ KI QS

41.	KN	JM	IL	HK	____	
42.	UA	XC	AE	DG	____	JK
43.	CS	BR	AQ	____	YO	
44.	ZY	BA	XW	DC	VU	____
45.	GA	HY	IW	____	KS	
46.	BC	XZ	EF	BD	HI	____

/6

Rearrange all the capital letters to form a correctly spelt word that will complete these sentences sensibly. Write the words on the answer lines.

Example

His pet rabbit was hungry so he fed him a juicy TOCARR. CARROT

47. The trumpets played a fanfare at the beginning of the MCEREYON. ______

48. The police SNTEGARE reassured the frightened lady. ______

49. There was a STSANALEDC competition on the beach. ______

50. Disaster struck when the tenor in the APEOR caught a cold. ______

51. The final match was very XITIEGCN. ______

52. The UPENSING were very comical to watch! ______

53. The cake was SLIOUCIDE. ______

54. The house was DTEECADOR for Christmas. ______

/8

Find the **relationship** between the **numbers** in the first two sets of brackets. The numbers in the third set of brackets are **related in the same way**. Find the missing number and add it to the final set of brackets.

Example

(6 [48] 8) (9 [45] 5) (7 [21] 3)

55. (11 [15] 4) (7 [16] 9) (19 [__] 12)

56. (9 [45] 5) (6 [36] 6) (7 [__] 6)

57. (24 [12] 2) (63 [9] 7) (84 [__] 7)

58. (2 [10] 4) (3 [26] 8) (9 [__] 8)

59. (2 [29] 5) (3 [25] 4) (2 [__] 7)

60. (48 [6] 8) (72 [8] 9) (27 [__] 3)

/6

/60

PAPER 15

In these questions, the pairs of letters are **linked** in some way. On the answer lines provided, write the **two** letters that complete the second pair, following the same pattern as the first. The alphabet has been provided to help you.

A B C D E F G H I J K L M N O P Q R S T U V W X Y Z

Example

BY is to **EV** as **HS** is to KP

1. **EG** is to **FH** as **RT** is to ________
2. **AD** is to **EH** as **MP** is to ________
3. **HF** is to **BA** as **XV** is to ________
4. **ZU** is to **PK** as **VQ** is to ________
5. **YX** is to **ZU** as **TS** is to ________
6. **PR** is to **QL** as **JL** is to ________

/6

7. Chloe, Katarina and Christopher need to collect 15 tokens to get a special offer the latest computer game.

   Katarina has 12 tokens. Chloe and Christopher each have more tokens than Katarina.

   If these statements are true, only one of the following statements **must** be true. Which one?

   A Christopher has the most tokens.

   B Chloe has the most tokens.

   C Christopher and Chloe can take advantage of the special offer.

   D Katarina can't take advantage of the special offer.

   E Christopher and Chloe can't take advantage of the special offer.

   ____

/1

8. Read the statements below, then answer the question.

Beth, Kate, William, Lance and Jay order a tray of milkshakes. Two are chocolate flavour, one is banana flavour, one strawberry flavour and one vanilla.

Beth only likes fruit flavour milkshakes.

Kate and William both chose the same flavour.

Jay doesn't like chocolate milkshake.

Lance ordered the banana milkshake.

Who ended up with the vanilla milkshake? ______________

/1

In the following questions, underline the **two** words, **one** from each set, that have a **similar meaning**.

Example

(car, take, jump) (chair, leap, drive)

9.	(predictable, featured, sporadic)	(frequent, even, irregular)
10.	(surprising, consistent, occasional)	(fascinating, boring, reliable)
11.	(carpenter, helper, apprentice)	(assistant, employer, director)
12.	(stripe, dashes, string)	(link, rope, fence)
13.	(boastful, bashful, courageous)	(faint, brave, wistful)
14.	(silence, whisper, sing)	(mention, song, murmur)
15.	(waterfall, power, machine)	(turbine, pipes, spray)
16.	(discrete, volatile, capacious)	(capacity, voluminous, carapace)

/8

In these questions, the word in capitals has had a group of **three** letters taken out. These three letters spell another word, without changing the order. Write the **three-letter** words on the lines provided. The sentences need to make sense.

Example

CABE and beans were her favourite vegetables. BAG

17. They all LISED carefully to the instructions. ______________

18. The SHERS worked each sheep quickly and deftly. ______________

19. 'How can I AGE without you?' ______________

20. The RROW flitted around the garden. ____________

21. She added the charm to her special BRLET. ____________

22. They watched as the rescue HELITER arrived. ____________

23. The fruit cake was full of nuts, sultanas and CURTS. ____________

24. The estate agent showed them many different HOS. ____________

/8

In the following questions, move **one** letter from the first word and add it to the second word to make two new words. Do **not** move any other letters. Write **both** new words, which **must make sense**, on the lines provided.

Example

ta**b**le reed → tale breed

25. rabid ounce → ____________ ____________

26. halve pear → ____________ ____________

27. float curt → ____________ ____________

28. black caste → ____________ ____________

29. knight laced → ____________ ____________

30. left able → ____________ ____________

31. scarf lowers → ____________ ____________

/7

Find the missing **pair of letters** in each sequence. The alphabet has been provided to help you.

A B C D E F G H I J K L M N O P Q R S T U V W X Y Z

Example

MO MK OQ KI QS

32. CQ DP FN IK ____

33. FE FG FD FI ____ FK

34. HY IX JW ______ LU

35. IA HY GW ______ ES

36. CG XP EC VT ______

37. WB UE SH QK ______

/6

Find **one** letter that will complete **both** pairs of words, finishing the first word and beginning the second word in each pair. The **same** letter must be used for both pairs of words. Write the letters on the lines provided.

Example

pa (t) ap hi (t)ime

38. de ______ in pa ______ hip

39. pea ______ ack boa ______ eap

40. sli ______ rawn hea ______ each

41. sea ______ oast figh ______ aper

42. loo ______ ale wor ______ alt

43. wil ______ ake sal ______ able

/6

In the following questions, underline the **two** words, **one** from each set, that will complete each sentence in the most sensible way.

Example

Head is to (face, arm, neck) as foot is to (leg, knee, thigh).

44. Ears are to (rings, sound, muff) as eyes are to (vision, shadow, glasses).

45. Boy is to (son, child, duke) as girl is to (mother, duchess, teacher).

46. Fork is to (lunch, cutlery, food) as plate is to (crockery, china, dish).

47. Metal is to (shiny, conductor, steel) as plastic is to (bendy, cheap, insulator).

48. Stallion is to (riding, mare, stable) as ram is to (horns, ewe, lambs).

49. Dirty is to (mud, clean, wash) and shiny is to (rub, foil, dull).

50. Winner is to (loser, victor, luck) as competitor is to (individual, contestant, athlete).

/7

To complete these questions, you need to **balance** the **numbers** on each side of the equation. Start by working out the calculation on the left. Next, find the missing number that will give the **same total** on the right-hand side.

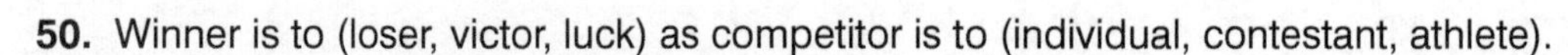

Example

$10 \times 6 \div 5 = 22 + 3 -$ [13]

51. $(7 + 4) - 2 = (15 +$ ________ $) - 9$

52. $4 \times 7 \div 2 = 9 + 7 -$ ________

53. $(11 + 13) - 3 =$ ________ $\times 5 - 4$

54. $\frac{(20 + 16)}{3} = 3($ ________ $+ 1)$

55. $\frac{(32 + 22)}{9} = \frac{(2 \times \text{\_\_\_\_\_\_\_\_})}{10}$

56. $3(5 \times 3) = \frac{(10 \times \text{\_\_\_\_\_\_\_\_})}{2}$

/6

These four words have been written as **number codes**, but one of the codes is missing. The words and codes are not necessarily in the same order. Write the answers to the questions on the lines provided.

STIR	REST	TEAR	STAR
3425	5463	6315	

57. Pick out the code for REST. ________

58. Pick out the word with the number code 3425. ________

59. What is the code for the missing word? ________

60. What does the code 6354436 spell? ________

/4

/60

PAPER 16

Write these words into the grids so that they can each be read across or down.

Example

YET EYE WET MEW AYE MAY

M	A	Y
E	Y	E
W	E	T

1. BYE CAT ONE TEE ANY COB

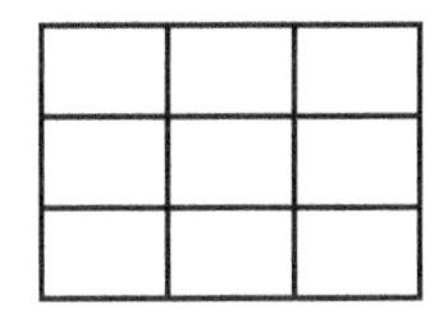

2. EGO TOE TEE BAT AGE BET

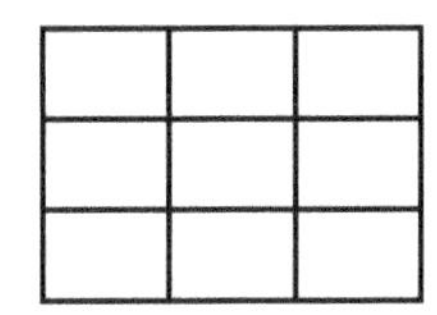

/2

In the first set of three words, the middle word has been made from letters in the other two words. Complete the second set of words in the **same** way to make the missing words, **which must make sense**. Write your answers on the lines provided.

Example

fast (tea) real leaf (fir) hire

3. soap (peas) fear earl (__________) gift
4. pint (rant) part fort (__________) post
5. glove (gear) large crate (__________) nasty
6. goose (store) otter bribe (__________) cared
7. wander (drawn) heard lately (__________) dated

8. whisk (show) whole party (________) grape

9. wealth (whale) water wallop (________) seats

10. worm (sour) fuss date (________) grip

/8

In the following questions, move **one** letter from the first word and add it to the second word to make two new words. Do **not** move any other letters. Write **both** new words, which **must make sense**, on the lines provided.

Example

table reed → *tale* *breed*

11. portent stung → ________ ________

12. splayed making → ________ ________

13. roman real → ________ ________

14. motor sewing → ________ ________

15. racking limb → ________ ________

16. amiss rely → ________ ________

/6

In the following sentences, a word of **four letters** is hidden across the **end** of one word and the **start** of the next word. Write the hidden words on the lines provided. The letter order must **not** be changed.

Example

The shop was la**st op**en on Tuesday. *stop*

17. Several new focus papers were launched. ________

18. The giant panda led the keeper into the den. ________

19. He was sorting one crate after the other. ________

20. She left early to catch the train. ________

21. He will also mention his new book. ________

22. The artist worked quickly to finish the painting. ________

/6

These four words have been written as **number codes**, but one of the codes is missing. The words and codes are not necessarily in the same order. Write the answers to the questions on the lines provided.

HOTTER	LETTER	TELLER	TOTTER
121136	421136	531136	

23. Pick out the code for TOTTER. ______________

24. Pick out the word with the number code 531136. ______________

25. Which word is missing a code? ______________

26. What is the code for the word in answer 25? ______________

WRITE	TWEET	TIERS	SWEET
41526	25613	34662	

27. Pick out the code for WRITE. ______________

28. Pick out the word with the number code 25613. ______________

29. Which word is missing a code? ______________

30. What would be the code for TRIESTE? ______________

/8

In the following questions, underline the **two** words, **one** from each set, that will complete each sentence in the most sensible way.

Example

Head is to (face, arm, neck) as foot is to (leg, knee, thigh).

31. Holiday is to (seaside, vacation, hotel) as footpath is to (road, hiking, pavement).

32. Landscape is to (view, painting, artist) as still life is to (frame, object, picture).

33. Leaf is to (bush, tea, branch) as bean is to (tree, coffee, seed).

34. Journalist is to (newspaper, headline, diary) as author is to (poetry, library, book).

35. Prairie is to (cattle, field, green) as mountain is to (brown, climbing, hill).

36. Ears are for (earrings, flapping, listening) as teeth are for (biting, brushing, dentists).

37. Frond is to (fern, weed, tree) as petal is to (stem, root, flower).

38. Old is to (grey, senile, ancient) as young is to (toddler, play, juvenile).

/8

In the following questions, underline the **two** words in each set that are **different** from the others.

Example

potato	lemon	banana	cabbage	strawberry

39.	chime	peel	peal	ring	tower
40.	scour	scrub	thorns	hunt	bush
41.	shell	hub	covering	crust	core
42.	abundant	scarce	profuse	copious	meagre
43.	pattern	taster	sequence	sample	trial
44.	lamb	kitten	mare	donkey	colt
45.	butterfly	eagle	beetle	wasp	bat
46.	beef	mutton	burger	pork	chop

/8

Underline the word that **cannot** be made from the letters of the word in capitals.

Example

HANDMADE	madden	head	demand	name	dream

47.	FESTIVAL	feast	live	flats	stove	fives
48.	PANCAKE	pack	keep	pane	neck	pace
49.	WONDERFUL	drone	flute	round	flew	drown
50.	SURPRISE	usurp	purrs	puss	super	spire
51.	MEDALLION	medal	lion	miner	nailed	modal
52.	CHOCOLATE	later	coal	cloth	halt	latch

/6

In each of the following questions, letters stand for numbers. Work out the answer to each sum. Write your answer as a **letter** on the line provided.

Example

If A = 2, B = 3, C = 4, D = 5, E = 6 and F = 8

what is the answer to this sum written as a letter? D + B = F

If A = 6, B = 3, C = 10, D = 24 and E = 7, what is the value of:

53. $A \times B + A =$ ________ **54.** $B \times A + A =$ ________

If A = 17, B = 6, C = 25, D = 3 and E = 7, what is the value of:

55. $B \times E - C =$ ________ **56.** $B \times D + E =$ ________

If A = 3, B = 7, C = 14, D = 21 and E = 5, what is the value of:

57. $D \div A + B =$ ________ **58.** $B \times E - D =$ ________

/6

Write these words into the grids so that they can each be read across or down.

Example

STEPS NEEDS LAPSE PLAIN APPLE POLES

P	O	L	E	S
L		A		T
A	P	P	L	E
I		S		P
N	E	E	D	S

59. HOSES SIDES RATED MARSH KITES MAKES

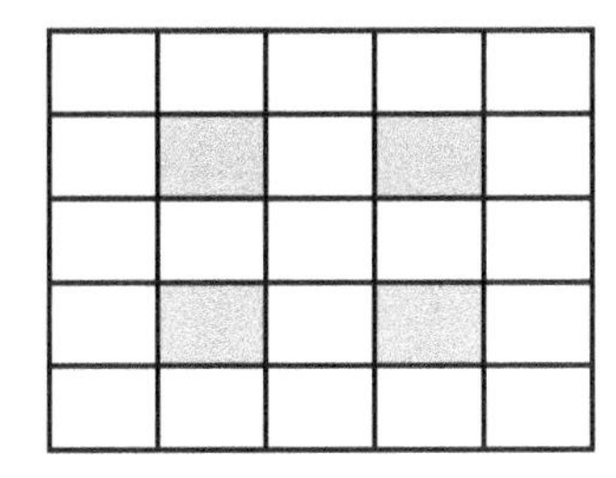

60. HOUSE OLDEN NEEDS DOUSE REEDS OTHER

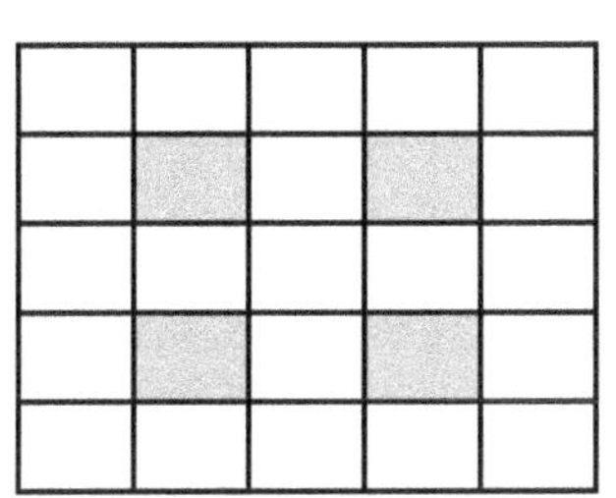

/2

/60

PAPER 17

In these questions, the pairs of letters are **linked** in some way. On the answer lines provided, write the **two** letters that complete the second pair, following the same pattern as the first. The alphabet has been provided to help you.

A B C D E F G H I J K L M N O P Q R S T U V W X Y Z

Example

BY is to **EV** as **HS** is to KP

1. **AB** is to **CE** as **LM** is to ________
2. **CD** is to **FG** as **PQ** is to ________
3. **WS** is to **TP** as **OK** is to ________
4. **BX** is to **FW** as **YU** is to ________
5. **YT** is to **UP** as **OJ** is to ________
6. **QN** is to **OP** as **LI** is to ________

/6

Write these words into the grids so that they can each be read across or down.

Example

YET EYE WET MEW AYE MAY

M	A	Y
E	Y	E
W	E	T

7. YOU AYE HUE ASH EYE SOY

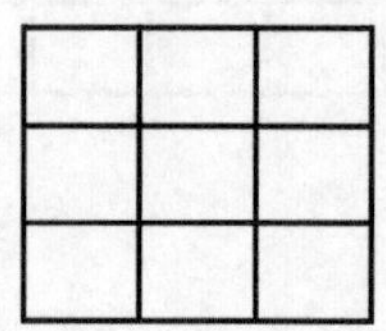

8. YET NET MAY AYE MEN EYE

/2

In the following questions, some words are written in code. The first code in the question has been solved for you. Use the **same** code to work out the second coded word. The alphabet will help you.

A B C D E F G H I J K L M N O P Q R S T U V W X Y Z

Example

If the code for DUCK is EVDL, what is the code for SWAN? TXBO

9. If the code for FINAL is HKPCN, what is the code for PLAIN? ______

10. If the code for COURT is BNTQS, what is the code for TRACE? ______

11. If the code for RANDOM is BKXNYW, what is the code for DREAM? ______

12. If the code for STAND is LMTGW, what does IKHNW mean? ______

13. If the code for BASIC is WVNDX, what does XVWGZ mean? ______

14. If the code for WAVES is EIDMA, what does DMQV mean? ______

/6

Underline the **two** words, **one** from each set, that when put together make one new, correctly spelt word. **The word from the group on the left always comes first**.

Example

(run, use, give) (take, less, red)

15. (wish, door, art) (top, let, way)

16. (tea, cloth, rank) (pot, rug, rag)

17. (cove, coast, calm) (red, lee, shed)
18. (car, for, far) (rot, gin, let)
19. (band, buck, wreck) (led, free, form)
20. (rote, tot, seep) (land, and, ally)
21. (row, sad, tog) (older, ether, ask)
22. (for, see, bay) (ward, wax, wood)

/8

Find the missing **pair of letters** in each sequence. The alphabet has been provided to help you.

A B C D E F G H I J K L M N O P Q R S T U V W X Y Z

Example

MO MK OQ KI QS

23. VZ GE UY CA ______ YW
24. LU JV HW ______ DY
25. MN OQ RU ______ AF
26. NA OZ MC PX ______ QV
27. ZC AF BI CL ______
28. PD SE TH ______ XL

/6

Find **one** letter that will complete **both** pairs of words, finishing the first word and beginning the second word in each pair. The **same** letter must be used for both pairs of words. Write the letters on the lines provided.

Example

pa (t) ap hi (t) ime

29. fer ______ ape lea ______ ote
30. bon ______ ver tam ______ ast
31. stea ______ ink stor ______ iosk

32. shar ____ angle chor ____ ash

33. crea ____ ettle for ____ ilk

34. leas ____ usk fis ____ aint

35. braw ____ ever mea ____ eech

36. cal ____ ocal thie ____ awn

/8

Underline the word that **cannot** be made from the letters of the word in capitals.

Example

HANDMADE	madden	head	demand	name	dream
37. PLEASANT	please	staple	plant	slant	pleat
38. WINTERY	wine	twin	wry	town	tyre
39. TELESCOPE	pelt	pole	cope	coat	steel
40. FOUNTAIN	faint	noun	often	font	faun
41. TRIUMPH	thump	trip	rump	hurt	tripe
42. HARMONY	moan	harm	maroon	roan	many

/6

In the following questions, underline the **two** words in each set that are **different** from the others.

Example

potato lemon banana cabbage strawberry

43. stone	cliff	rock	boulder	gorge
44. contemporary	present	past	current	dated
45. individual	crowd	gang	crew	couple
46. coupons	ration	allocation	sample	share
47. money	purse	currency	wallet	cash
48. rich	poor	wealthy	prosperous	famous
49. whales	dolphins	elephants	sharks	eels
50. spectacle	display	shower	exhibit	glasses

/8

These four words have been written as **codes**, but one of the codes is missing. The words and codes are not necessarily in the same order. Write the answers to the questions on the lines provided.

DELAY LADLE DEALT TALLY

%>@@! @>£@* £*>@%

51. Pick out the code for TALLY. ______

52. Pick out the word with the code @>£@*. ______

53. Which word is missing a code? ______

54. What is the code for the word in answer 53? ______

MANGER RANGER MANAGE GARAGE

w t f s d w c t f t s d c t f s d w

55. Pick out the code for MANAGE. ______

56. Pick out the word with the code w t f s d w. ______

57. Which word is missing a code? ______

/7

In each of the following questions, letters stand for numbers. Work out the answer to each sum. Write your answer as a **letter** on the line provided.

Example

If A = 2, B = 3, C = 4, D = 5, E = 6 and F = 8

what is the answer to this sum written as a letter? D + B = F

If A = 8, B = 3, C = 9, D = 2 and E = 11, what is the value of:

58. C ÷ B + A = ______

59. A ÷ D + C − D = ______

60. E + C − A − B = ______

/3

/60

PAPER 18

1. Aeroplanes A, B and C fly from New Town airport to Hong Kong.

   Aeroplane A leaves New Town at 7.00am.

   Aeroplane B takes twice as long to fly to Hong Kong as Aeroplane C.

   Aeroplane B leaves two hours after Aeroplane A and arrives at 9.00pm.

   Aeroplane C arrives at 3.00pm.

   If these statements are true, only one of the following statements **must** be true. Which one?

   A Aeroplane C takes off at 9.00am.

   B Aeroplane A is the first to land.

   C There are only three flights from New Town to Hong Kong each day.

   D All three aeroplanes follow the same flight path.

   E Aeroplane A was delayed at take-off. ________________

   /1

2. Read the statements below, then answer the question.

   Jamal, David, Ian, Claire and Rebecca are in the same class at school.

   In a maths test they score 18, 16, 14, 13 and 9, but these scores are not in name order.

   David got one mark higher than Jamal. Claire got twice as many marks as Ian.

   What was Rebecca's score? ________________

   /1

In the following questions, underline the **two** words, **one** from each set, that have a **similar meaning**.

Example

(car, take, jump) (chair, leap, drive)

3. (approximate, devise, specific) (precise, inaccurate, monitor)
4. (bonfire, tip, rubble) (scaffolding, debris, clearance)
5. (preside, prestige, powerful) (statue, status, pontificate)
6. (stone, chisel, sculpture) (carving, artistic, wood)

7. (throw, anorak, scarf) (cape, blanket, monocle)

8. (tunnel, pipe, dike) (canal, marsh, ditch)

9. (placard, magazine, signpost) (strike, hoarding, advertisement)

10. (vision, modern, design) (architect, map, plan)

/8

In these questions, the word in capitals has had a group of **three** letters taken out. These three letters spell another word, without changing the order. Write the **three-letter** words on the lines provided. The sentences need to make sense.

Example

CABE and beans were her favourite vegetables. BAG

11. The old SERT looked after the rich lady. ______

12. The bright SLET dress was her favourite colour! ______

13. They were rescued from the EMKMENT. ______

14. The box was full of local PUCE. ______

15. They had an excellent lunch in the CANN. ______

16. It was late when the PY finished. ______

/6

Find the missing **pair of letters** in each sequence. The alphabet has been provided to help you.

A B C D E F G H I J K L M N O P Q R S T U V W X Y Z

Example

MO MK OQ KI QS

17. QN RL SJ TH ______

18. MK RF WA ______ GQ

19. SZ	RY	PW	______	IP	
20. TA	VE	XI	ZM	______	
21. FW	LT	RQ	______	DK	
22. GI	RN	FH	SO	EG	______
23. AD	BF	CF	DH	EH	______
24. XM	WL	UJ	TI	______	

/8

In the following questions, move **one** letter from the first word and add it to the second word to make two new words. Do **not** move any other letters. Write **both** new words, which **must make sense**, on the lines provided.

Example

ta**b**le reed → *tale* *breed*

25. petal tiling → ______ ______

26. crane sauce → ______ ______

27. choke allow → ______ ______

28. glass win → ______ ______

29. flatten wit → ______ ______

30. whines self → ______ ______

31. clover panting → ______ ______

32. weaves laden → ______ ______

/8

In the following sentences, a word of **four letters** is hidden across the **end** of one word and the **start** of the next word. Write the hidden words on the lines provided. The letter order must **not** be changed.

Example

The shop was la**st op**en on Tuesday. stop

33. The debris kept falling from the rafters. ____________

34. It was time to get the roof fixed. ____________

35. He was sent all the way back again. ____________

36. He must ice the cake for her birthday. ____________

37. We will ban knives from our public places. ____________

38. They had a picnic one day. ____________

/6

In the following questions, underline the **two** words in each set that are **different** from the others.

Example

potato lemon banana cabbage strawberry

39. climate	rain	hail	sun	snow
40. forest	prairie	orchard	plain	copse
41. comedian	giggle	joker	chuckle	laugh
42. bicycle	wheelbarrow	tricycle	motorbike	scooter
43. box	plastic	chest	cardboard	container
44. hutch	trough	sty	stable	gate
45. peril	danger	accident	hazard	safety
46. emergency	hurricane	crisis	tornado	typhoon

/8

The last word can be formed from the first word by changing three letters. Each letter-change creates a correctly spelt word. Write in the missing words in the spaces provided. The order of the letters does not change.

Example

SWAN swam swim SLIM

47. POST ________ ________ PANE

48. CART ________ ________ MORE

49. NEST ________ ________ WANT

50. PANE ________ ________ LAMP

51. WISE ________ ________ CASH

52. LINE ________ ________ PUNK

/6

Rearrange all the capital letters to form a correctly spelt word that will complete these sentences sensibly. Write the words on the answer lines.

Example

His pet rabbit was hungry so he fed him a juicy TOCARR. CARROT

53. The children ate too much CATHOLECO cake at the party! ________

54. Get all the PSAEEART ingredients ready first. ________

55. They took the dogs for a long walk in the YCRUOTN. ________

56. She set off, determined to complete the ISONSMI. ________

57. They were totally lost in the fog without a PSCMAOS. ________

58. They could see snow on the distant INOMUTASN. ________

59. The old grey GOAAONRK had a very strong tail. ________

60. The children's band even had a BOTNMORE player. ________

/8

/60

Progress grid

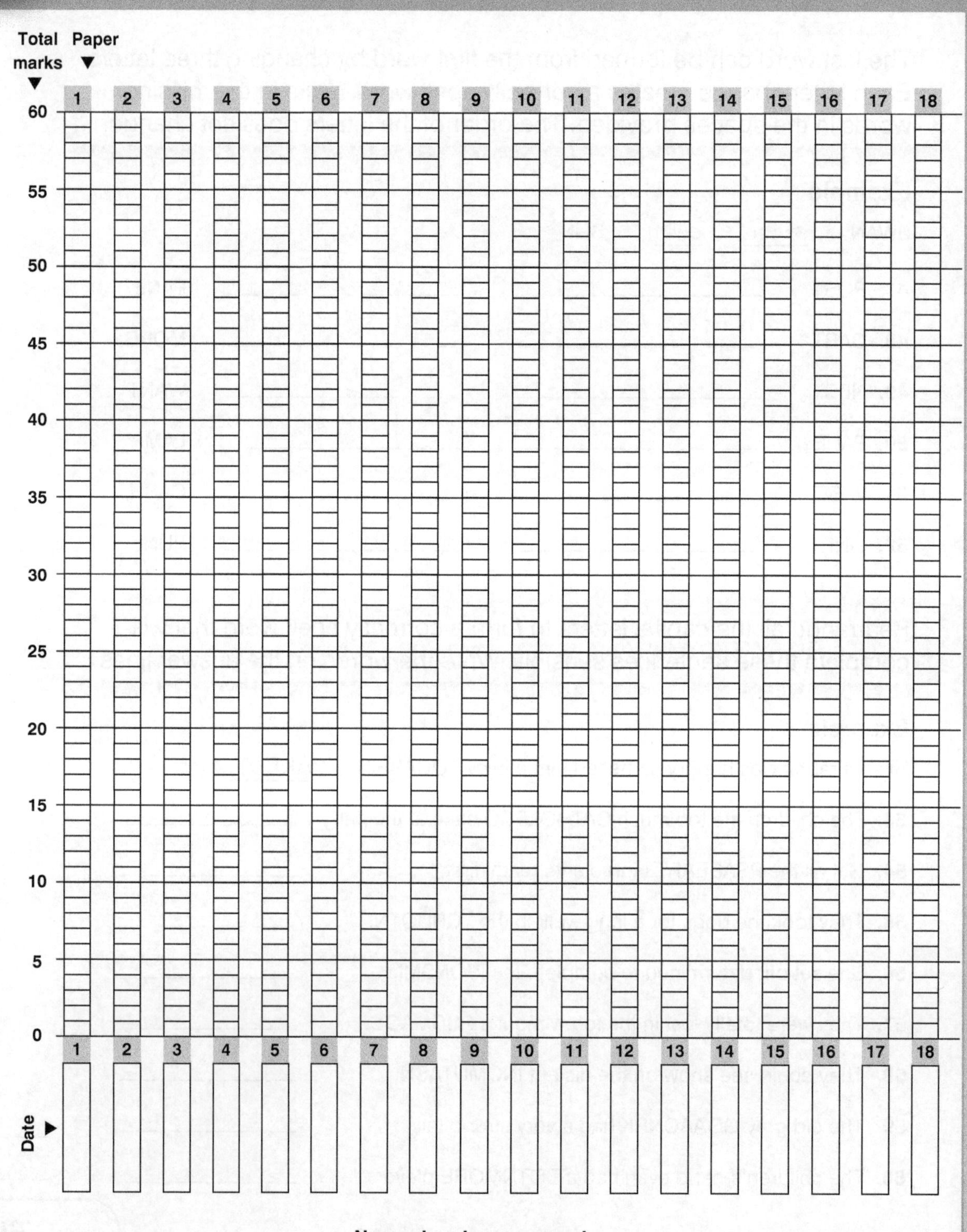

Now colour in your score!

Verbal Reasoning Age 10–11 Assessment Papers Answers

Paper 1

1. hunt, search
2. help, assist
3. teach, instruct
4. slumber, sleep
5. run, sprint
6. burden, load
7. cash, money
8. worry, anxiety
9. book
10. stick
11. perch
12. direct
13. bow
14. wound
15. refuse
16. lock
17. reason training
18. crochet thought
19. wait dessert/deserts
20. fond brook
21. room brink
22. flow kneel
23. ore
24. foal
25. moat
26. crate
27. sour
28. tilt
29. lute
30. saint
31. YZ
32. UX
33. XU
34. PM
35. OM
36. QK
37. RN
38. HD
39.

E	B	B
A	Y	E
R	E	D

(Answers may vary as the positioning of the grid can change)

40.

T	O	E
O	W	N
R	E	D

(Answers may vary as the positioning of the grid can change)

41. volcano, earthquake
42. June, October
43. plastic, cotton
44. buttercup, daisy
45. delighted, cheerful
46. singer, conductor
47. clay, drawing
48. wind, cloud
49. C
50. D
51. A
52. C
53. B
54. A
55. pots
56. ache
57. pace
58. noose
59. thin
60. dare

Paper 2

1. rise, fall
2. sharp, blunt
3. create, destroy
4. accept, reject
5. congratulate, commiserate
6. capture, release
7. considerable, negligible
8. assist, hinder
9. PIN
10. ATE
11. ANT
12. CAR
13. ASH
14. ANT
15. ILL
16. HUB
17. here
18. mean
19. near
20. form
21. vest
22. hare
23. weal
24. toad
25. AK
26. TS
27. RP
28. WR
29. MQ
30. MH
31. SYMPHONY
32. SUPPORT
33. PUNCTUALLY
34. CAMELS
35. POURING
36. NEWSPAPER
37. DRAGONFLIES
38. FORECAST
39. 11
40. 42
41. 9
42. 51
43. 5
44. 4
45. 8
46. 15
47. 2
48. 4
49. paint
50. burner
51. slots
52. cat
53. wane
54. paddle
55. cold, slow
56. red, blue
57. light, dark
58. time, distance
59. feather, scale
60. season, day

Paper 3

1. pole
2. eager
3. noun
4. weir
5. wool
6. deal
7. least
8. waif
9. 1354
10. DEER
11. WEED
12. 2334
13. 32561
14. HEATS
15. SHEET
16. 41563
17. forget
18. bargain
19. office
20. fortnight
21. forage
22. brandish
23. hostage
24. cutlass
25. JQ
26. QK
27. KN
28. NJ
29. YW
30. KI
31. AY
32. DL
33. C
34. 12:00
35. SBHF
36. PQVIB
37. ZKTVX
38. MINE
39. SEND
40. SDMA
41. CRATE
42. YAWN
43. ash hip, fish hot
44. mind darn, fled deep
45. rear rind, roar ripe
46. drew watch, claw wary
47. wand dent, ward dawn
48. leak keep, soak kilt
49. slay yet, story yarn
50. mask kerb, husk keep
51. A
52. D
53. B
54. E
55. C
56. E
57. tail
58. player
59. feather
60. midge

Paper 4

1. 12, 24
2. 2, 8
3. 16, 26
4. 9, 36
5. 10, 12
6. 12, 15
7. 4, 6
8. 11, 3
9. hopper chart
10. salon mouse
11. tread arch
12. money knave
13. fast storey
14. manger beast
15. maze minister
16. rigid faster
17. thus
18. bend
19. mall
20. yare/area/real
21. this
22. hiss/soft
23.

P	O	P
E	V	E
W	A	N

(Answers may vary as the positioning of the grid can change)

24.

T	O	T
A	R	E
P	E	N

(Answers may vary as the positioning of the grid can change)

25. knife, fork
26. paper, message
27. shawl, cloak
28. hum, whistle
29. natural, organic
30. vineyard, orchard
31. reject, separate
32. water, wires
33. KN
34. KQ
35. ON
36. GF
37. OR
38. TG
39. E
40. C
41. B
42. Y
43. W
44. Z
45. CURRENT
46. QUEUES
47. SUSPENSION
48. TEMPERATURE
49. STALAGMITES
50. LABELLED
51. APRICOTS
52. DICTIONARY
53. pane
54. pith
55. why
56. them
57. flowery
58. lisp
59. tan
60.

W	A	T	C	H
I		O		U
L	A	T	E	R
T		A		R
S	I	L	L	Y

(Answers may vary as the positioning of the grid can change)

Paper 5

1. moorland heath
2. machine engine
3. funny humorous
4. angry irate
5. fowl poultry
6. verse rhyme
7. spade shovel
8. cable wire
9. puppies, lions
10. courage, hope

11. chips, butter 12. wind, snow
13. key, string 14. material, hair
15. autumn, winter 16. butterfly, frog
17. 26 18. 10
19. 10 20. 12
21. 15 22. 25
23. 17 24. 47
25. lab 26. rusted
27. ram 28. pets
29. bonnet
30. ERA 31. ACT
32. EAT 33. LED
34. PIN 35. CAT
36. EAR 37. HAM
38. neat 39. them
40. some/omen 41. sees
42. hebe/wasp 43. love/vert
44. hero 45. twin
46. C
47. Tuesday
48. C 49. E
50. B 51. A
52. B
53. mop pin, gap pea
54. park kelp, fork kick
55. hail leap, feel long
56. bear rack, pour ripe
57. scour rune, fear rant
58. neap pine, flap pair
59. spurt tarn, cart team
60. pier rail, steer rock

Paper 6

1. contest 2. bandage
3. handsome 4. knowledge
5. inspire 6. rather
7. captor 8. nappies
9. paste 10. spar
11. treat 12. claw
13. deter 14. dream
15. tones 16. adder
17. 21 18. 48
19. 3 20. 32
21. 72 22. 16
23. UW 24. OF
25. QW 26. NJ
27. SH 28. MI
29. NQ 30. RI
31.

M	E	N
A	G	O
T	O	W

(Answers may vary as the positioning of the grid can change)

32.

T	E	A
A	M	P
D	U	E

(Answers may vary as the positioning of the grid can change)

33. divide, split
34. pray, mutter
35. bread, jam 36. run, march
37. return, arrive 38. smooth, regular
39. sanity, shock 40. wire, chain
41. IV 42. CV
43. QU 44. PJ
45. BF 46. SQ
47. cinder 48. sting
49. hinder 50. sit
51. amp 52. spins
53. grain 54. full
55. nice 56. chopper
57. field 58. dinner
59. town 60. scent

Paper 7

1. row win, few war
2. sap pod, nip pew
3. posy year, ploy yawn
4. tram mast, form must
5. lace east, lame earn
6. corm mare, warm meat
7. plumb barn, herb brand
8. wart town, foot trot
9. band 10. rock
11. score 12. lift
13. block 14. ring
15. point 16. match
17. older scarf
18. beach hearth
19. traced knight
20. whiter/wither tenth
21. patent claim
22. vale pound
23. raid pounce
24. miss relay
25. KIT 26. ATE
27. EAR 28. VIE
29. RID 30. DID
31. ONE 32. SEA
33. river 34. mound
35. relay 36. tuft
37. really 38. dinted
39. motor 40. plate
41. D
42. north-west
43. PR, EG 44. QR, WX
45. EG, FH 46. SN, YE
47. PJ, EW 48. YE, OY
49. DE, XD 50. MG, EF
51. MOUNTAIN 52. SCRATCHED
53. SATELLITE 54. DETECTIVE
55. PEACOCKS 56. MARATHON
57. THEATRE 58. AUTHOR
59.

P	R	O	U	D
A		V		U
S	T	E	M	S
T		R		T
E	N	T	R	Y

(Answers may vary as the positioning of the grid can change)

60.

R	O	C	K	S
A		A		T
P	A	N	S	Y
I		O		L
D	A	N	C	E

(Answers may vary as the positioning of the grid can change)

Paper 8

1. probe, prod
2. gleeful, jovial
3. miserable, despondent
4. ambition, aspiration
5. stroll, wander 6. push, shove
7. ask, enquire 8. swell, enlarge
9. sea, earth 10. kennel, stable
11. pie, sandwich 12. beef, mutton
13. synonyms, definitions
14. oven, fridge
15. 216534 16. TABLET
17. BEASTS 18. 546212
19. 54261 20. PRODS
21. PEERS 22. 62413
23. leap 24. pear
25. route 26. silk
27. teams 28. wrap
29. slope 30. grape
31. JMYL 32. WGJVO
33. URYSJ 34. BANJO
35. FOUND 36. XHWIA
37. GROANS 38. GREEN
39. 5 40. 11
41. 4 42. 2
43. 5 44. 9
45. lean 46. rim
47. trip 48. rid
49. rule 50. congregate
51. drain 52. mail
53. struts 54. wrist
55. trump
56. D 57. D
58. A 59. E
60. D

Paper 9

1. 18 2. 56
3. 6 4. 92
5. 10 6. 41
7. 60
8. straw, hay
9. sole, palm 10. numbers, words
11. flower, tree 12. patient, client
13. chemistry, physics
14. wrong, correct
15. stop, go
16. leaflet 17. postage
18. scarlet 19. betray
20. option 21. bowled
22. caraway 23. sealant
24. stir 25. goal
26. echo/hand 27. peas
28. seam/isle 29. gout
30. hebe/arch 31. hate
32.

A	T	E
P	E	A
T	A	T

(Answers may vary as the positioning of the grid can change)

33.

C	E	P
O	V	A
N	E	W

(Answers may vary as the positioning of the grid can change)

34. shed, garage
35. variable, unpredictable
36. mature, increase
37. money, merit
38. yoghurt, grated
39. wheelbarrow, bucket
40. pilgrimage 41. hot
42. scare 43. cap
44. cry 45. tape
46. lit
47. hit toy, art tin
48. leaf fail, loaf face
49. talk kick, rack keen
50. feat test, beat talk
51. grown none, grain north
52. nail list, foal land
53. mean near, darn norm
54. lamb beach, slab barn
55. gauge 56. niche
57. marry 58. stint
59. reams 60. talker

Paper 10

1. chorus, refrain
2. slip, slither
3. brush, sweep
4. cooperate, collaborate
5. exhibit, display
6. desk, bureau
7. threaten, intimidate
8. cherish, value

9. lean — 10. catch
11. produce — 12. board
13. break — 14. tap
15. lap — 16. cape
17. ocular jargon
18. review spender
19. ream scale
20. trice threat
21. revel forage
22. winkle frail
23. plane native
24. actor function
25. MO — 26. VS
27. ZX — 28. ZG
29. MK — 30. HS
31. OJ — 32. JH
33. eagle, chicken — 34. snack, banquet
35. barometer, candle — 36. detain, invite
37. slug, squid — 38. fear, battle
39. rubber, ruler — 40. volcano, cave
41. dream — 42. red
43. more — 44. rash
45. pet — 46. spotter
47. D — 48. E
49. C — 50. A
51. A — 52. B

Answers for questions 53–60 may vary:

53. MINE, DINE — 54. BOLT, BOAT
55. BEER, SEER — 56. WINE, WIND
57. SHOP, SHIP — 58. BIND, BOND
59. CONE, CANE — 60. BULL, BALL

Paper 11

1. arrive, leave — 2. commence, conclude
3. squander, hoard — 4. biased, fair
5. advance, retreat — 6. notice, ignore
7. 46151 — 8. VERSE
9. RISES — 10. 26414
11. 362251 — 12. RETAIL
13. RETIRE — 14. 152435
15. coal, water — 16. left, reverse
17. queen, countess
18. night, day
19. dusk, evening
20. voices, instruments
21. PUT — 22. RAG
23. LEG — 24. HER
25. LOG — 26. HIS/HIM
27. ARC — 28. FOR
29. hand/putt — 30. hebe/tank
31. heat — 32. raft
33. leap — 34. tour
35. sand — 36. nest
37. E
38. Chris
39. KM — 40. HF
41. NM — 42. BA
43. ZJ — 44. LG
45. ALPHABETICAL
46. RESERVOIR
47. FOREST
48. OSTRICH
49. DEPARTURE
50. RESTAURANT
51. skim moon, beam mean
52. grit take, wart tour
53. grout tear, sort tore
54. stare emit, lame elope
55. single, alone
56. fierce, ferocious
57. bank, slope
58. Earth, globe
59. quarrel, argument
60. nation, country

Paper 12

Answers for questions 1–6 may vary:

1. MINT TINT
2. FINE FIND
3. RIPE RISE
4. DAME DIME
5. BEST BENT
6. PILL PULL
7. rise, ascend
8. comedy, tragedy
9. bottle, jar
10. nest, drey
11. red, green
12. end, conclusion
13. portray — 14. livestock
15. seaside — 16. bitten
17. wither — 18. season
19. notice — 20. sundry
21.

C	A	N
O	R	E
W	E	T

(Answers may vary as the positioning of the grid can change)

22.

B	A	N
I	C	E
D	E	W

(Answers may vary as the positioning of the grid can change)

23. desert, wilderness
24. daylight, hibernating
25. skip, tiptoe
26. learn, follow
27. edge, height
28. carrots, rhubarb
29. valuable, rare
30. peak, ridge
31. NO, QR — 32. IN, RY
33. ZW, JG — 34. SH, GT
35. CE, RT — 36. DA, VS
37. RO, ZG — 38. ZY, DU
39. 15, 24 — 40. 20, 24
41. 32, 128 — 42. 25, 36
43. 2, 10 — 44. 18, 12
45. 21, 12 — 46. 7, 63
47. 24123 — 48. NORTH
49. THORN — 50. 23546
51. 21356 — 52. SLAPS
53. STEAL — 54. 216354
55. gout — 56. serve
57. pilau — 58. pride
59. wines — 60. coat

PAPER 13

1. angel cherub
2. flourish brandish
3. wound injure
4. stretch extend
5. flee escape
6. question interrogate
7. famous eminent
8. reward recompense
9. scales, thermometer
10. knitting, sewing
11. young, youth
12. princess, duchess
13. flock, pack
14. eggs, fish
15. wood, metal
16. cheese, bone
17. crow pendant
18. rockery insect
19. mat toaster
20. budge stage
21. tread wash
22. rouse linger
23. dram severe
24. stave beret
25. 563226 — 26. REVIVE
27. RIVERS — 28. 341235
29. 6152 — 30. PINT
31. TIME — 32. 3253
33. MAN — 34. CAN
35. ATE — 36. BAR
37. HER — 38. TAN
39. WIN — 40. RAT
41. D — 42. 12.10pm
43. WARDROBE
44. ENVELOPE
45. DONKEYS
46. COMPETITION
47. VINTAGE
48. CANDYFLOSS
49. OMELETTE
50. CONGRATULATIONS
51. E — 52. D
53. B — 54. C
55. C — 56. C
57. cotton — 58. ravens
59. metre — 60. magic

PAPER 14

1. fresh, stale — 2. banish, welcome
3. precarious, stable — 4. delight, disappoint
5. elation, despair — 6. slight, stocky
7. secure, uncertain — 8. condemn, pardon
9. bandage — 10. scarecrow
11. button — 12. bargain
13. nestled — 14. tattoo
15. rumbled — 16. tearing
17. hope — 18. hoot
19. gain — 20. tent
21. brawl — 22. stir
23. lean — 24. leak
25. trip — 26. carp
27. tent — 28. pins
29. self — 30. rump
31. wasp — 32. rate
33. 30 — 34. 13
35. 25 — 36. 28
37. 4 — 38. 11
39. 14 — 40. 27
41. GJ — 42. GI
43. ZP — 44. FE
45. JU — 46. FH
47. CEREMONY
48. SERGEANT
49. SANDCASTLE
50. OPERA
51. EXCITING — 52. PENGUINS
53. DELICIOUS — 54. DECORATED
55. 31 — 56. 42
57. 12 — 58. 74
59. 53 — 60. 9

PAPER 15

1. SU — 2. QT
3. RQ — 4. LG
5. UP — 6. KF
7. D — 8. Jay

9. sporadic irregular
10. consistent reliable
11. helper assistant
12. string rope
13. courageous brave
14. whisper murmur
15. machine turbine
16. capacious voluminous
17. TEN **18.** ARE/EAR
19. MAN **20.** SPA
21. ACE **22.** COP
23. RAN **24.** USE
25. raid bounce
26. have pearl
27. flat court
28. back castle
29. night lacked
30. let fable
31. scar flowers
32. MG **33.** FC
34. KV **35.** FU
36. GY **37.** ON
38. dew win, paw whip
39. poor rack, boar reap
40. slip prawn, heap peach
41. seat toast, fight taper
42. loom male, warm malt
43. wilt take, salt table
44. sound vision
45. duke duchess
46. cutlery crockery
47. conductor insulator
48. mare ewe
49. clean dull
50. victor contestant
51. 3 **52.** 2
53. 5 **54.** 3
55. 30 **56.** 9
57. 5463
58. TEAR
59. 6325
60. STREETS

PAPER 16

1.

C	A	T
O	N	E
B	Y	E

(Answers may vary as the positioning of the grid can change)

2.

B	A	T
E	G	O
T	E	E

(Answers may vary as the positioning of the grid can change)

3. life **4.** sort
5. teas **6.** bride
7. dealt **8.** trap
9. spelt **10.** part
11. potent strung
12. played masking/makings
13. roan realm
14. moor stewing
15. raking climb
16. miss relay
17. cusp **18.** dale/peri
19. gone **20.** tear
21. some/omen **22.** hear
23. 121136 **24.** LETTER
25. TELLER **26.** 135536
27. 41526 **28.** TIERS
29. TWEET **30.** 2156326
31. vacation, pavement
32. view, object
33. tea, coffee
34. newspaper, book
35. field, hill
36. listening, biting
37. fern, flower
38. ancient, juvenile
39. peel, tower
40. scour, hunt
41. hub, core
42. scarce, meagre
43. pattern, sequence
44. mare, donkey
45. eagle, bat
46. burger, chop
47. stove **48.** keep
49. flute **50.** usurp
51. miner **52.** later
53. D **54.** D
55. A **56.** C
57. C **58.** C
59.

M	A	R	S	H
A		A		O
K	I	T	E	S
E		E		E
S	I	D	E	S

(Answers may vary as the positioning of the grid can change)

60.

O	L	D	E	N
T		O		E
H	O	U	S	E
E		S		D
R	E	E	D	S

(Answers may vary as the positioning of the grid can change)

PAPER 17

1. NP **2.** ST
3. LH **4.** CT
5. KF **6.** JK
7.

A	S	H
Y	O	U
E	Y	E

(Answers may vary as the positioning of the grid can change)

8.

M	E	N
A	Y	E
Y	E	T

(Answers may vary as the positioning of the grid can change)

9. RNCKP **10.** SQZBD
11. NBOKW **12.** PROUD
13. CABLE **14.** VEIN
15. doorway **16.** teapot
17. covered **18.** carrot
19. buckled **20.** totally
21. together **22.** forward
23. TX **24.** FX
25. VZ **26.** LE
27. DO **28.** WI
29. fern nape, lean note
30. bone ever, tame east
31. steak kink, stork kiosk
32. shard dangle, chord dash
33. cream mettle, form milk
34. least tusk, fist taint
35. brawl lever, meal leech
36. calf focal, thief fawn
37. please **38.** town
39. coat **40.** often
41. tripe **42.** maroon
43. cliff, gorge
44. past, dated
45. individual, couple
46. coupons, sample
47. purse, wallet
48. poor, famous
49. sharks, eels
50. shower, glasses
51. %>@@! **52.** LADLE
53. DELAY **54.** £*@>!
55. c t f t s d **56.** RANGER
57. GARAGE **58.** E
59. E **60.** C

PAPER 18

1. A
2. 16
3. specific precise
4. rubble debris
5. prestige status
6. sculpture carving
7. throw blanket
8. dike ditch
9. placard hoarding
10. design plan
11. VAN **12.** CAR
13. BAN **14.** ROD
15. TEE **16.** ART
17. UF **18.** BV
19. MT **20.** BQ
21. XN **22.** TP
23. FJ **24.** RG
25. peal tilting
26. cane saucer
27. coke hallow
28. lass wing
29. fatten wilt
30. wines shelf
31. cover planting
32. waves leaden
33. risk **34.** hero
35. tall **36.** emus/herb
37. bank **38.** cone
39. climate, sun
40. prairie, plain
41. comedian, joker
42. wheelbarrow, tricycle
43. plastic, cardboard
44. trough, gate
45. accident, safety
46. emergency, crisis

Answers for questions 47–52 may vary:

47. PAST PANT
48. CARE CORE
49. WEST WENT
50. LANE LAME
51. WISH WASH
52. PINE PINK
53. CHOCOLATE
54. SEPARATE
55. COUNTRY
56. MISSION
57. COMPASS
58. MOUNTAINS
59. KANGAROO
60. TROMBONE